The Shell Book of How Cars Work

Edited by
Stuart Bladon

Adam & Charles Black · London

Second edition, 1983 by
A & C Black (Publishers) Ltd
35 Bedford Row, London WC1R 4JH

Originally published 1963–4 as four
separate books
One volume edition by Gordon
Walmsley first published 1966 by John
Baker Publishers, Ltd.

© Shell UK Limited, 1983, 1966

Second edition originally published in
The Netherlands under the title *Zo
weerkt een auto* by Shell Nederland
Verkoopmaatschappij B.V., Rotterdam

The Shell book of how cars work.
—2nd ed.
   1. Automobiles
   I. Bladon, Stuart
   629.2'222   TL145

   ISBN 0-7136-2392-6
   ISBN 0-7136-2257-1 Pbk

ISBN 0-7136-2392-6
ISBN 0-7136-2257-1

Phototypeset by MS Filmsetting
Limited, Frome, Somerset
Printed by The Stanborough Press
Limited, Grantham, Lincolnshire

Contents

The Engine

The basic principles

The engine

The fuel system

The ignition system

The cooling system

The lubrication system

The complete engine

The diesel engine

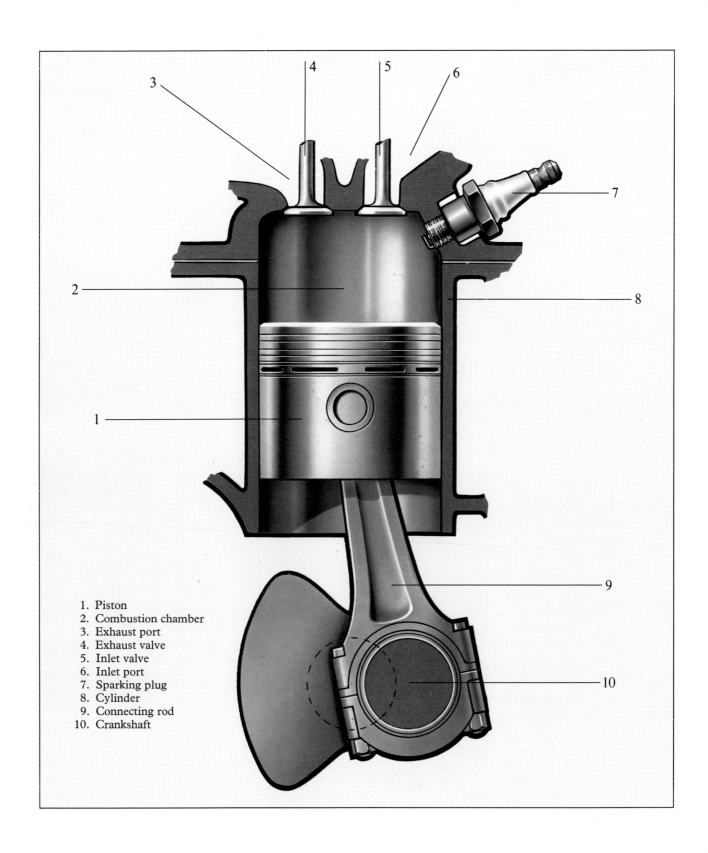

1. Piston
2. Combustion chamber
3. Exhaust port
4. Exhaust valve
5. Inlet valve
6. Inlet port
7. Sparking plug
8. Cylinder
9. Connecting rod
10. Crankshaft

The basic principles

At first sight a car engine looks like a complex piece of machinery, but it is actually not so complicated as might be supposed. Its basic principles are quite simple, and once these are grasped you will have no trouble distinguishing between an engine's main and secondary functions.

What happens inside an engine is basically this: fuel is burned and the heat that this burning generates is converted into the energy needed to propel the car forward.

As you know, the fuel used in most car engines is petrol, just one of many products refined from crude oil. The most important feature of petrol is that it is particularly inflammable when mixed with the right amount of air, and a tiny spark will be sufficient to ignite such a mixture in an instant.

In a car engine, a mixture of air and petrol is compressed in an enclosed space and then ignited. The heat from this combustion quickly expands the gases, developing great pressure. This expansion force is released in a straight line and the same principle as used in an old-fashioned treadle sewing machine is used to turn this into a rotary motion which eventually drives the wheels of a car.

It goes without saying that this burning or combustion process cannot be left to its own devices, and with the aid of a number of ingenious mechanisms we are able to control the combustion so as to be able to make use of the released energy in the best possible way. The illustration opposite shows the essential components of an engine.

First, there is the cylinder. This is a tube, closed at the top, in which the piston can move up and down. The part of the cylinder above the upper limit of piston travel is called the combustion chamber, and it is into here that the inflammable mixture of air and petrol is introduced. As the piston descends, this mixture is first sucked in and is then compressed as the piston, having reached its lower limit of travel, starts to rise again. At the correct instant, with the piston near its upper limit again, and the mixture now fully compressed, an electric spark from the sparking plug ignites the compressed charge of fuel/air mixture. The burning gases quickly expand, pushing the piston back downwards. To turn this 'up-and-down' motion into a rotary motion, the piston is connected to the crank or crankshaft via the connecting rod.

Finally, openings are needed to allow the burned gases to escape and to admit fresh mixture into the combustion chamber. This happens via the exhaust and inlet ports respectively, both of which are closed by means of valves during the appropriate phases of the engine sequence.

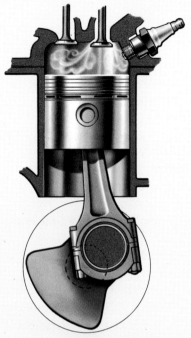

1. Induction

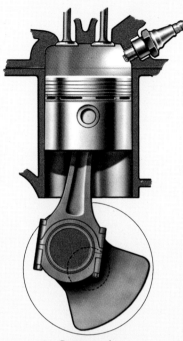

2. Compression

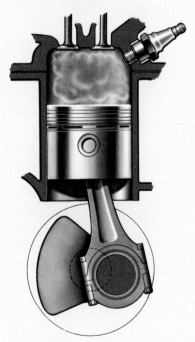

3. Expansion or power

4. Exhaust

One combustion stroke to every four strokes

In nearly every car engine, the piston has to do four strokes (i.e. twice up and down) for every time the air/petrol mixture is ignited in the cylinder. The other strokes are needed to fill and empty the cylinder and to compress the mixture, as we shall see.

Let's start with the piston in its uppermost position. As the engine's starter motor turns the crankshaft, the piston moves downwards. By means of a mechanism which we shall explain later, the inlet valve is opened, allowing the air/petrol mixture to be sucked into the cylinder (fig. 1). When the piston has arrived at the bottom of its travel the 'induction stroke' is complete and the inlet valve closes.

As the crankshaft continues to turn, the piston is pushed upwards again, compressing the mixture inside the combustion chamber (fig. 2) – this is the 'compression stroke'.

Towards the end of the compression stroke, the sparking plug gives off a spark which ignites the mixture, causing a rapid rise in temperature with the result that the gases expand and push the piston back down. This expansion (or power) stroke turns the crankshaft, and the engine can now run under its own power (fig. 3).

When the piston reaches the bottom of the power stroke the exhaust valve is opened and the piston commences its fourth and final stroke, the exhaust stroke (fig. 4). As it rises, it forces the burned gases out of the cylinder. The exhaust valve is then closed and we are back where we started! The whole process can begin afresh, and will be repeated again and again so long as there is a fresh supply of air and petrol.

Because this process consists of four strokes, we call it the four-strokes principle, and an engine that works on this principle is a four-stroke engine. There are engines that work on a two-stroke principle, but they are not used in cars any more, only in some motor-cycles and lawnmowers, motor scooters and small marine engines.

So far we have just been talking about one cylinder only, but modern engines always have at least two, and some have six or eight cylinders. However, the average engine has four, and the following chapter is based on this four-cylinder engine. Each of the four cylinders works in exactly the same way as the one described above, but they are not all on the same stroke at the same time.

The engine

Usually when we say 'engine' we mean more or less everything under the bonnet of a car, but in fact there are four distinct parts:

- the engine itself, together with its lubricating system
- the fuel system
- the ignition system, and
- the cooling system.

First let us take a closer look at the actual engine, its components and what they do. As we said in the last chapter, we shall concentrate on the type of engine that is most commonly found, the four-cylinder.

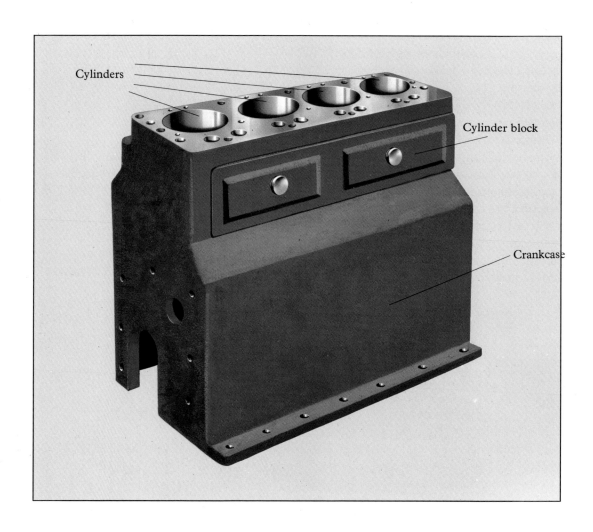

Cylinders

Cylinder block

Crankcase

The cylinder block and crankcase

Piston

Piston rings

The biggest part of the engine, the engine block, consists of the cylinder block and the crankcase. In most engines, these two parts form a whole, but in some engines they are two separate units joined together with bolts.

The cylinders are accurately formed bores in the cylinder block, into which the pistons fit precisely yet freely enough to be able to move up and down. To prevent exhaust gases from escaping between the piston and the cylinder wall, the piston must be sealed against the cylinder, and so it is provided with a number of circular grooves containing spring-loaded rings that press outward against the wall of the cylinder. The uppermost rings are called compression rings, while those below are the oil control rings, so-called because part of their job is to control the supply of oil to the upper parts of the piston.

Each piston is fixed by means of a gudgeon pin to a connecting rod and in such a way that the rod is able to pivot in either direction. The lower end of the connecting rod is attached to the crankshaft via a bearing. This bearing, the well-known 'big end', consists of two sections held together with bolts.

Piston

Gudgeon pin

Connecting rod

Big-end

Crankshaft

The crankshaft is one of the most important parts of an engine, since it provides the rotary motion that is needed to turn the car's wheels. The crankshaft's job is not an easy one, since it has to withstand not only the enormous forces that are exerted upon it but also the high speeds at which it must turn, several thousand times per minute in an average engine. This is why the crankshaft is provided with counterweights so that it can rotate at high speed without vibrating.

The crankshaft is carried in a number of main bearings, and the position of the cranks on the crankshaft shows that two of the pistons make their strokes at different times from the other two: while the two outermost pistons are at the top position, the inside pistons are right down at the bottom of their cylinders.

At the end of the crankshaft is a heavy wheel, the flywheel, whose sheer weight gives the crankshaft the inertia to keep turning between firing impulses, and ensures that the engine runs smoothly. As you can see, the flywheel is provided with teeth that form the starter ring. When you turn your car's ignition key, a little gear-wheel on the starter motor rotates, at the same time moving forward along a spiral shaft, so that it engages with this ring and turns the flywheel. Thus the crankshaft is also made to rotate; the

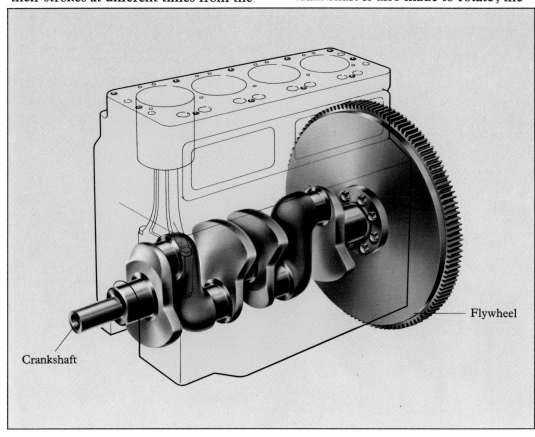

Crankshaft

Flywheel

engine is now being forced to run under electrical power from the battery, and the petrol-burning sequence can now begin and will then take over so that the starter motor is no longer needed, until the next time the engine is to be started.

At the other end of the crankshaft is another wheel which drives the camshaft. Formerly, the camshaft used to be carried inside the block of the engine, and was driven by chain from this wheel on the nose of the crankshaft. More usually today it is carried on the top of the engine – an overhead camshaft, as it is called – and is driven by a special belt with teeth on its inner face.

The camshaft's function is to operate the inlet and exhaust valves, ensuring that they open and close at just the right time. As the shaft turns, each cam – there is one cam for every valve – bears against a cylindrical block, the tappet, which in turn pushes up the pushrod that operates the valve mechanism. We shall come back to the valve mechanism in a moment.

Underneath, the crankcase is enclosed by a metal pan, the sump, which contains the oil that lubricates the engine. When the oil is old, it can be drained off by removing a plug in the bottom of the sump.

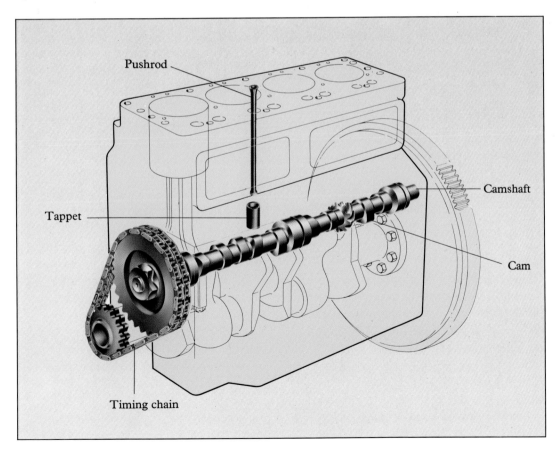

Pushrod

Camshaft

Tappet

Cam

Timing chain

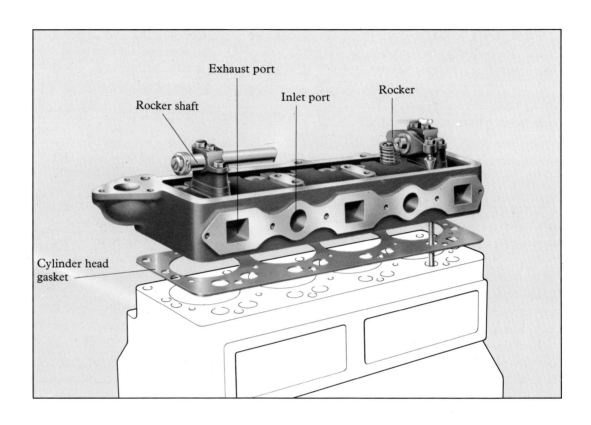

Exhaust port

Rocker shaft

Inlet port

Rocker

Cylinder head gasket

The cylinder head

The cylinder head is mounted on top of the cylinder block. It contains the inlet and exhaust valves, the valve mechanism and the sparking plugs. The cylinder head is bolted to the block, and between the adjacent faces is a seal – the cylinder head gasket – which prevents gas from leaking.

The inlet ports in the cylinder head are joined to the inlet manifold – a solid assembly of pipes – through which the mixture of air and petrol enters the cylinder from the carburettor. For the exhaust ports there is an exhaust manifold which takes the exhaust gases away to the exhaust system.

Each cylinder has two valves, an inlet valve which admits the air/petrol mixture, and an exhaust valve past which the gases escape after combustion.

When at rest, each valve is pressed against its seat in the inlet or exhaust

14

port by means of a strong spring, ensuring that nothing can enter or escape from the cylinder. The valves are opened by a mechanism, which works like this: as the camshaft rotates, a cam bears against a tappet which in turn pushes a pushrod upwards. This causes a rocker to pivot on the rocker shaft, pressing down on the valve stem, and causing the valve to open.

Between the rocker and the valve stem there is a little gap, the valve clearance. This clearance is important – if it were not there, the valve would not close completely owing to heat expansion, and thus precious combustion gases would escape and the engine would lose power.

The valve mechanism is enclosed by a cover (the valve or rocker cover) which is bolted to the top of the cylin-der head. The whole mechanism is constantly supplied with lubricating oil. Another seal is placed between the cover and the cylinder head to prevent this oil from leaking.

As explained earlier, the position of the camshaft can vary, and in many engines it is carried on the cylinder head, not in the cylinder block. This kind of engine with its 'overhead camshaft' – often abbreviated to ohc – has no need to pushrods, since the camshaft comes in direct contact with the rockers, or even bears directly against 'inverted bucket' cam followers on top of the ends of the valves. The overhead camshaft system is preferable, since it reduces the reciprocating weight of the valve gear. A slight drawback is that it is not so convenient to provide adjustment for wear.

1. Valve shut
2. Camshaft
3. Tappet
4. Pushrod
5. Rocker shaft
6. Rocker
7. Valve spring
8. Valve
9. Valve open

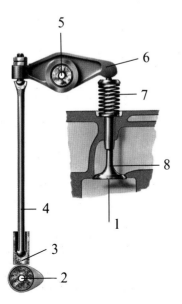

The fuel system

The mixture of air and petrol which the engine needs is provided by the fuel system which consists of the petrol tank, the petrol pump, a filter, and the carburettor.

The petrol pump ensures a steady supply of fuel to the carburettor, and can be mounted next to the petrol tank itself or – as the illustration shows – next to the engine, in which case the pump is usually mechanically operated by the camshaft, otherwise it is electrically operated.

All fuel systems, mechanical or electric, have fine filters to stop tiny particles of corrosion and dirt that might be in the petrol tank from getting into the engine and damaging it or, more likely, blocking the tiny jets in the carburettor.

The supply of air is just as important as the supply of petrol. About 8000 litres of air are needed for the combustion of one litre of petrol, and the two are mixed in just the right proportion by the carburettor. In addition, the carburettor allows us to adjust the amount of combustible mixture so that we can control the rotational speed and the power of the engine. The carburettor is mounted on the inlet manifold, a system of pipes which takes the air/petrol mixture to the inlet ports of the cylinders.

Carburettors are very varied in design as well as being usually rather complex, so we shall confine our description to the basic principles starting from a hypothetical, simplified version.

The carburettor contains a petrol reservoir called the float chamber which is kept constantly supplied with fuel by the petrol pump. The level of

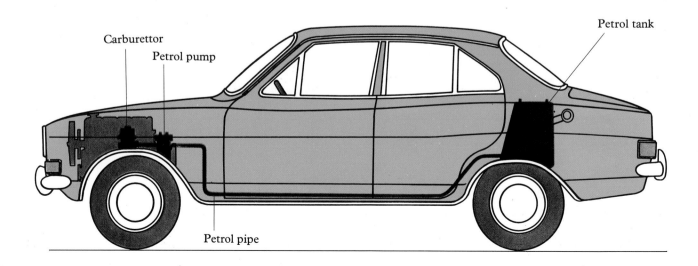

Carburettor

Petrol pump

Petrol tank

Petrol pipe

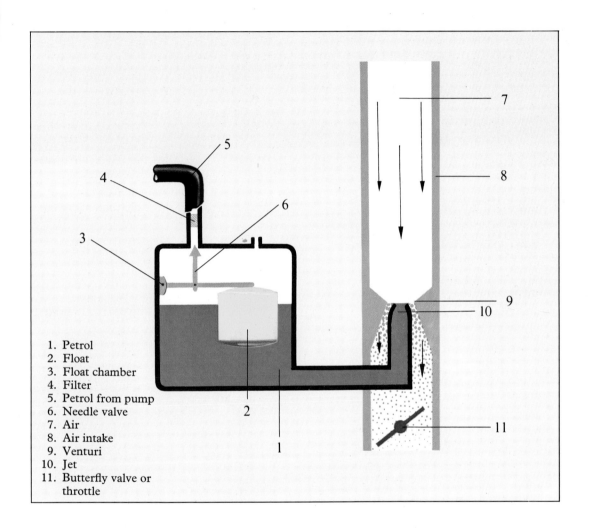

1. Petrol
2. Float
3. Float chamber
4. Filter
5. Petrol from pump
6. Needle valve
7. Air
8. Air intake
9. Venturi
10. Jet
11. Butterfly valve or throttle

the fuel is maintained by a float which shuts off the fuel supply (by means of the needle valve) when the correct level is reached.

From the float chamber, the petrol flows to a jet which is positioned in a narrow section of the air intake tube called the venturi. As the engine runs and each cylinder makes its intake stroke in turn, air is drawn into the engine through the venturi. Inside the venturi the air is mixed with the petrol which is present as tiny droplets at first, but is later turned to vapour, aided by the heat of the engine.

The amount of combustible mixture

17

that reaches the cylinders is regulated by the throttle valve which is located in the venturi in front of the inlet manifold, and is operated by the accelerator pedal.

Above the carburettor there is an air filter which removes dirt and other pollutants from the incoming air and so gives the engine added protection against wear and tear.

As we said before, for every litre of petrol, 8000 litres of air are needed on average: 'on average', because the precise proportion depends on how you drive. If, for instance, you press hard on the accelerator there will be a sudden rush of air into the venturi which will not be followed immediately by an increased supply of petrol. To keep the engine going therefore, most carburettors are provided with an extra jet, the so-called acceleration jet, which comes into operation as required.

Quite a different proportion of air to petrol is needed when starting an engine from cold. A cold engine needs a 'richer' mixture, which means the percentage of petrol is greater than normal. In some engines this richer mixture is obtained by means of a separate cold-start carburettor that supplies extra petrol for starting. In other types, the venturi incorporates a valve – the choke valve – which reduces the amount of air entering the carburettor.

Chokes themselves can be of different types: some are operated by hand from inside the car, although more and more cars are being fitted with automatic chokes that operate according to the engine's temperature.

Fuel injection

In engines with one carburettor only, it is not easy to ensure that each cylinder is supplied with just the right mixture of air and petrol. The droplets of fuel tend to choose the line of least resistance with the result that the middle cylinders get an over-rich mixture while the mixture in the outer cylinders is too weak.

One answer to this problem is to use two or more carburettors, but this raises difficulties in terms of matching and tuning the individual carburettors with each other.

An alternative to the carburettor system is the method of supplying a metered quantity of petrol to each cylinder, known as fuel injection. Basically, a fuel injection system consists of an injection nozzle for each cylinder and a special type of pump. The petrol can be injected either directly into the cylinder or into the inlet port, or even into the inlet manifold.

The ignition system

The purpose of the ignition system is to provide a spark in each cylinder at the right moment, so that the mixture of air and petrol will ignite. Basically the ignition system consists of three parts: the coil, the distributor and the sparking plugs.

When starting, the electric current required for the ignition system is supplied by the car battery, which is

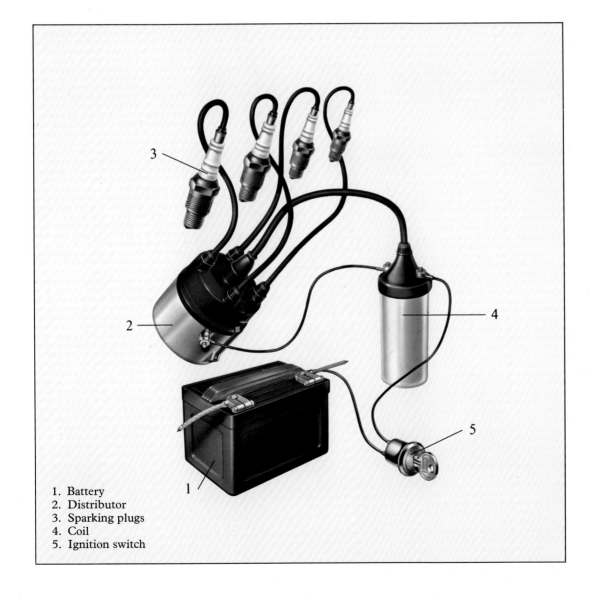

1. Battery
2. Distributor
3. Sparking plugs
4. Coil
5. Ignition switch

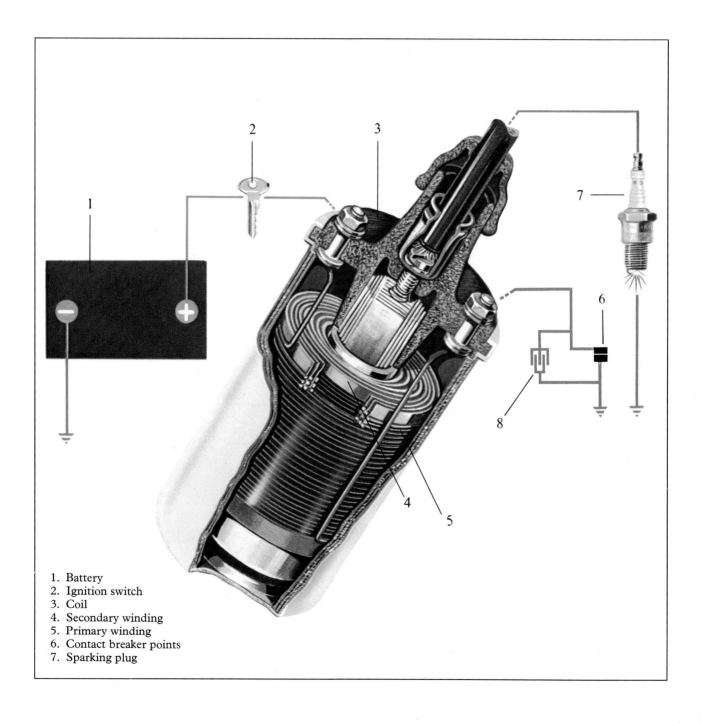

1. Battery
2. Ignition switch
3. Coil
4. Secondary winding
5. Primary winding
6. Contact breaker points
7. Sparking plug

charged by the dynamo once the engine is running. The dynamo's current however is low in tension (usually 12 volts), while a high tension current is required to make the spark jump in the combustion chamber of the cylinder – around 15 000 volts or more.

The low tension current is converted to high tension current by means of the coil which is actually two coils of insultated wire wound around a soft iron core. The outer, or primary, coil consists of relatively thick wire and is fed from the battery.

Inside the primary coil is the secondary coil comprising a much greater number of windings of very thin wire. The coil works like this: current from the battery flows through the primary coil causing a magnetic field in the soft metal core which suddenly disappears when the current is interrupted. This generates a very high tension in the secondary coil for an instant, high enough to produce the spark that is needed to ignite the mixture inside the cylinder. The tension (i.e. voltage) of the spark depends on the number of windings in the two coils. For example, if the number of windings in the secondary coil is 1250 times greater than those in the primary coil, then the result is a voltage of 1250×12 volts $= 15\,000$ volts.

The sudden interruption in current to the primary coil is caused by the contact breaker, which is housed inside the unit known as the distributor. The distributor consists of a housing with a central shaft that is rotated by a skew gear off the camshaft. The top end of this shaft has a four-lobe cam (or six lobes if the engine has six cylinders) mounted on it which, as it rotates, opens and closes the contact points, so interrupting the current.

The high tension thus generated in the coil is returned to the distributor which then does the job for which it is named – distributing the current to the sparking plugs at the correct moment, and in the correct order.

The actual distribution process takes place inside the distributor head, a cover made of insulting material which is mounted on top of the distributor housing. The distributor head contains four contacts (one for each cylinder) plus a central contact which receives the high tension current from the coil. The incoming current is transmitted via a carbon brush to the rotor arm – an insulated component with a strip of metal which creates a connection with each plug contact in turn as the rotor arm rotates. Thus each sparking plug receives in turn a pulse of current which produces the necessary spark.

The sparking plug itself consists of a metal body that is screwed into the cylinder head and which incorporates two electrodes separated from each other by insulating material (porcelain). In the middle is the central electrode that is connected to one of the high tension contacts inside the distributor cap. At the bottom of the plug is the second or side electrode that is separ-

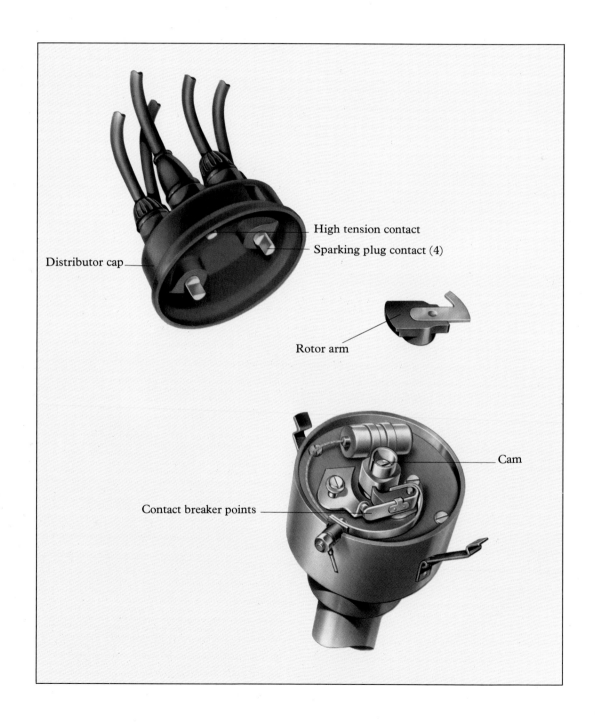

High tension contact

Sparking plug contact (4)

Distributor cap

Rotor arm

Cam

Contact breaker points

ated from the central electrode by a few tenths of a millimetre.

Whenever a high tension pulse is passed by the distributor to the plug, it passes down the central electrode, jumps the gap to the side electrode, and makes a spark that ignites the mixture of air and petrol. Contrary to what you might think, the spark is not made at precisely the moment when the piston reaches its topmost point. It is made a little earlier, so that the combustion pressure is at its maximum as the piston passes its highest point and the best possible expansion effect is obtained. As the engine turns faster the spark has to be made even earlier, and this is achieved by means of the timing advance mechanism which is built into the distributor.

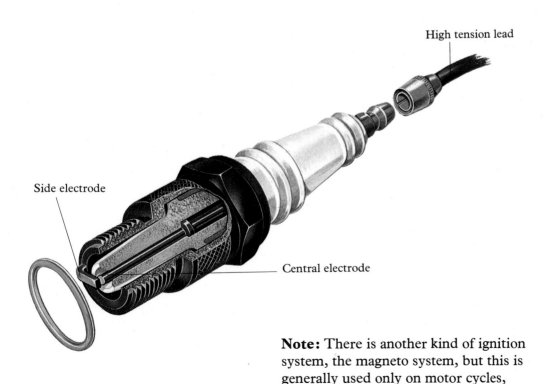

High tension lead

Side electrode

Central electrode

Note: There is another kind of ignition system, the magneto system, but this is generally used only on motor cycles, scooters and small marine engines.

The cooling system

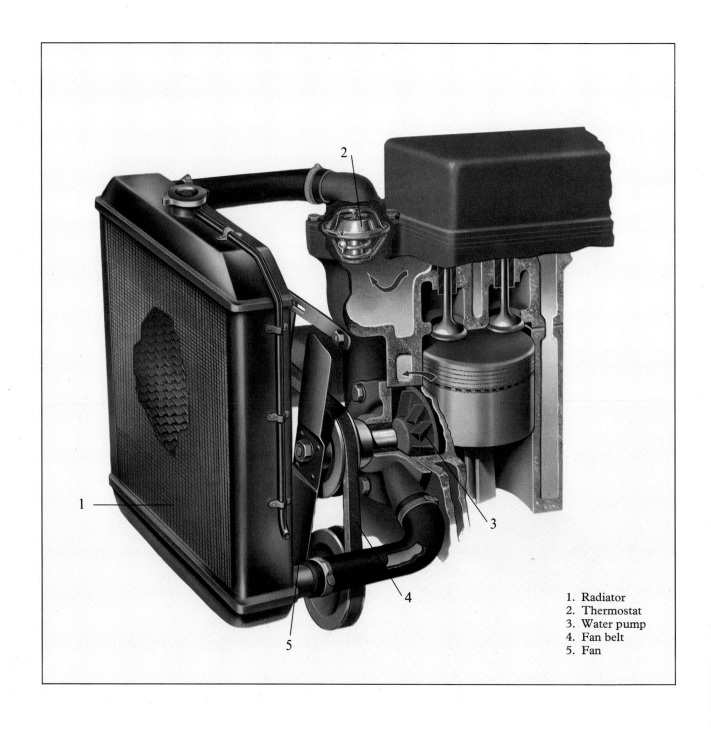

1. Radiator
2. Thermostat
3. Water pump
4. Fan belt
5. Fan

The combustion process that takes place inside the engine obviously generates a lot of heat, far more than is actually needed. It is a fact that the average petrol engine converts at most only about 25 per cent of the energy stored in the fuel into mechanical energy, while the rest is lost in the form of heat passed to the cooling system and the exhaust. This heat is, of course, not useless, since it can be employed to warm the interior of the car in winter.

The cooling system is needed to regulate the engine operating temperature. Car engines can be cooled by water or air, although the great majority now have water cooling.

The engine's cylinders are surrounded by 'jackets' – special passages which contain the water that absorbs the excess heat. It is a simple law of nature that hot water is lighter than cold water, and so it rises and returns to the radiator. This system – called thermosyphon – was adequate for the simple cars of the past, but had limitations of efficiency and space, since it was necessary for the water to be able to rise directly to the radiator 'header' tank. Nowadays, the lower fronts of cars call for the header tank to be much lower down, and for this and other reasons all cars have a water pump to circulate the cooling water.

The radiator itself consists of a large number of small tubes; as you drive along, the passage of air through the radiator cools the water inside. A fan, driven from the crankshaft by the same vee-belt (or fan belt) that drives the water pump and the electrical generator, assists cooling by maintaining air flow through the radiator when the car is at rest or moving very slowly – as in city traffic. These days, many cars have electrically-driven fans which work only when necessary.

As mentioned earlier, the cooling system is also used to heat the passenger compartment of your car. Some of the hot coolant water flows through the heater radiator and supplies warmth to the interior.

An engine's ideal running temperature is around 85 °C, and the thermostat makes sure that the temperature of the coolant never falls too far below this level during normal running. It acts like a valve, shutting off the flow to the radiator when the temperature is too low, and opening progressively as the temperature rises above the normal running heat. Feed to the heater is separate, so that the heater is kept warm, and in winter the flow to the radiator may often be very small indeed.

The coolant water could, of course, freeze in winter, because with the circulation cut off by the thermostat for much of the time, the water in the radiator would be trapped and 'static', while exposed to the icy blast of the car's forward motion. Also, while the car was parked, even the water surrounding the cylinders could freeze, causing damage to the engine. To prevent this, we add anti-freeze to the water. Good anti-freeze has an anti-corrosion effect, and so should be left in the cooling system all year round; but because the anti-corrosion additives eventually are exhausted, anti-freeze needs to be renewed at the start of every winter.

The lubrication system

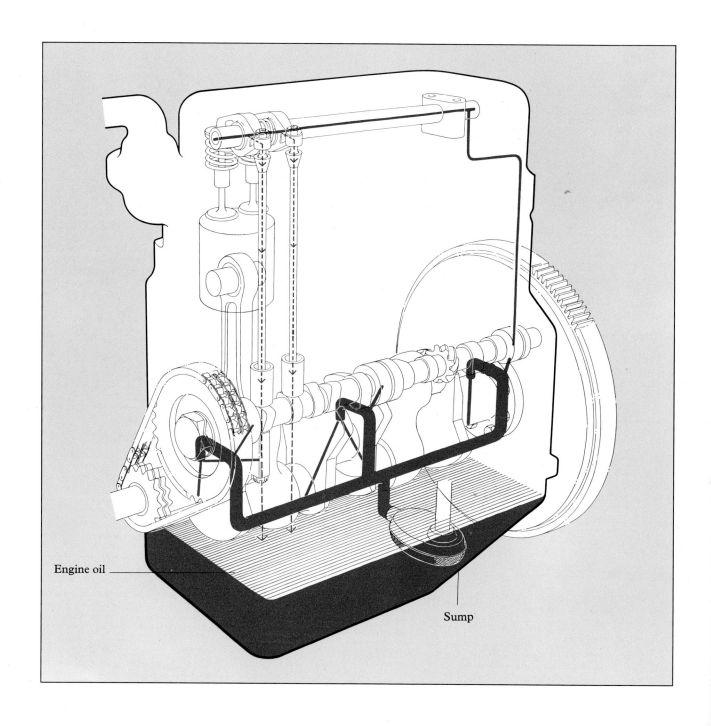

Engine oil

Sump

The lubrication system is one part of the engine whose importance is frequently underestimated.

The flow of oil is necessary for several reasons. First it reduces friction and wear of the moving parts, and second the oil 'cools' the bearings, pistons and other components. In addition, the lubricant improves the seal between the pistons and the cylinder wall, preventing the 'blow-by' of combustion gases past the piston rings. Finally, the oil keeps the inside of the engine clean, and combustion residue is removed when the engine oil is changed.

Most engines have a 'force-feed' or pressure lubricating system. A pump draws oil from the sump and forces it through a filter and then through channels – the oilways – to the bearings of the crankshaft and camshaft and also to the valve mechanism. At the same time, oil flowing from the bearings forms an oil mist in the crankcase, and this lubricates the cylinder walls.

A warning light or oil pressure gauge is usually provided inside the car so that the driver will know when the system is not functioning and the oil not circulating properly.

The complete engine

Now we have seen broadly how the engine and its auxiliary systems function, it is time to take a look at the complete engine installation. We will find that there are a few parts which we have not yet talked about.

The 'sizes' of an engine

Not all cars have the same 'size' of engine. After all, one car is bigger or heavier than another and so needs a more powerful engine.

The problem is that there are many different ways of giving the 'size' of an engine, and these are often confused, and confusing! Even more puzzling is the use of all sorts of units by which the sizes are given. Here are a few of the more common terms together with the units in which they are given.

Engine capacity

How powerful an engine is depends, of course, on the capacity of its cylinders: the bigger the cylinders, the greater the amount of fuel mixture they can burn and the greater the force that is exerted upon the pistons.

The engine capacity is sometimes called the 'swept volume' and the meaning of this expression becomes clear when we consider each cylinder in turn. The swept volume is in fact that part of the cylinder which the piston 'sweeps' in one stroke and is calculated from the bore (diameter) of the cylinder and the stroke, i.e. the distance travelled by the piston in the cylinder between its top and bottom points. Thus the uppermost part of the cylinder, the combustion chamber, is not counted.

The engine capacity of modern passenger cars varies from around 600 to over 5000 cc (cc = cubic centimetre; 1000 cc = 1 litre). This is why an engine with a capacity of 2000 cc is also referred to as a '2-litre engine'.

Compression ratio

The power of an engine is also determined by the compression ratio, which indicates the extent to which the fuel mixture is compressed inside the cylinder.

The illustration on the next page shows how the compression ratio is calculated. If the capacity ($V1$) of the cylinder plus combustion chamber is, say, 400 cc, and the capacity of the combustion chamber alone ($V2$) is 50 cc., then the compression ratio is 400:50, or 8:1. (We can also see that the swept volume in our example is 350 cc, since the combustion chamber is not counted.)

The fact that engine powers have increased so much in recent years is partly due to an increase in compression ratios. As the compression ratio rises, the mixture of fuel and air in the cylinder is compressed more, causing a greater combustion force. However, the compression ratio cannot be increased beyond certain limits for reasons we shall see in the later chapter on 'Petrol'.

Torque

The performance of an engine naturally depends upon the force that is exerted on the pistons by the combustion pressure. One measure of this force is torque, an expression often used in advertisements and test reports, but which can still cause confusion.

Put simply, torque is the force with which a shaft is turned round. A good example of this is tightening a car's wheel nuts with a four-way wrench. Two arms of the wrench are used as a lever, while the other two act as a shaft. The force that is exerted on the 'shaft' is called torque.

It is clear that the torque can be increased in one of two ways: either by exerting more force on the levers or exerting the same amount of force on longer levers. The torque can be calculated by multiplying the force exerted on the lever by the length of the lever arm. Torque is currently

measured in Britain by the self-explanatory term 'lb/ft' – giving clear relation between force, as a measure of mass or weight, and distance (in feet), being the length of the lever. The metric term now often in use is Newton meres, abbreviated to Nm. The old unit of kilogram force (kgfm) is still to be found.

(1 Nm = approx. 0.1 kgfm, or
1 Nm = 1.383 lb/ft).

The engine torque usually given in motor manufacturers' advertising is therefore the force with which the crankshaft rotates. The torque can also serve as a measure for comparing the pulling power of different cars.

Now one might think that as the engine runs faster, i.e. as the crankshaft rotates more quickly, the torque remains constant because the combustion force also stays the same; but it does not quite work like that in practice. As the pistons move faster, the cylinders have less time to fill up with fresh mixture. This causes the combustion pressure to drop and so the torque decreases as well. An engine usually attains its maximum torque at around half of its maximum turning speed.

Power

By the power of an engine, we mean the amount of work which the engine can do in a certain time.

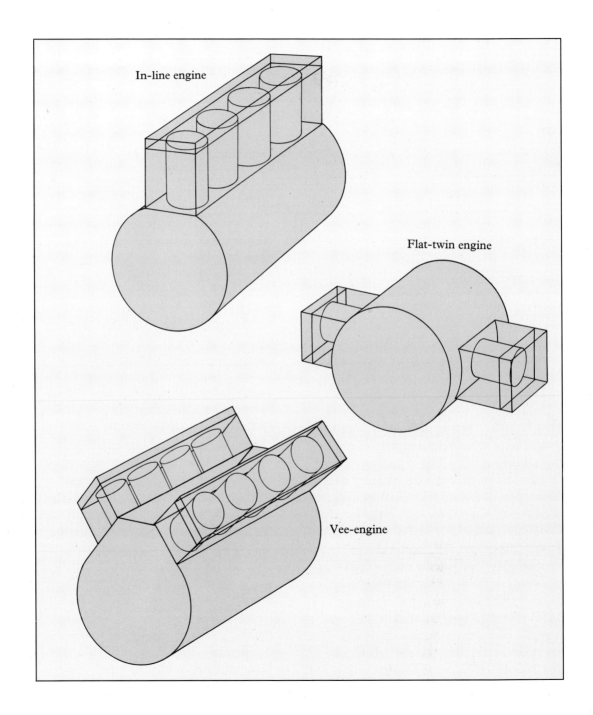

In-line engine

Flat-twin engine

Vee-engine

The power also depends on the number of times that force is exerted on the pistons in a given time unit. There is a big difference whether the torque can be used 1000 or 5000 times per minute.

This is why the power of an engine increases as the crankshaft rotates faster. Here again, we see that at very high engine speeds the power begins to decrease for the same reasons that the torque falls off after a certain engine speed is reached.

The car manufacturer therefore indicates a maximum engine speed (in rpm = revolutions per minute) which lies at or just before the point where the engine begins to lose power – higher engine speeds would be just pointless.

An engine's power used to be given in HP (horsepower) and measurement in brake horse power (bhp) is still widely used in Britain. Since the introduction of the new international system of units (SI) this is now tending to be done in kW (kilowatts). The table below gives a rough comparison of the various units.

Table

1 HP = 75 kgfm/s
1 kW = 1.36 HP
The power of an engine is measured differently in certain countries, but there is usually some indication of which system is being used.

Other types of engine

So far we have just been talking about an engine with 4 cylinders arranged one behind the other because this is the type most commonly found. However, there is a large number of different types of engine both as regards the number and layout of the cylinders.

The number of cylinders can vary widely, with engines having 1, 2, 3, 4, 5, 6, 8 or 12 cylinders. As regards cylinder layout, this is not so varied, and there are three basic types:

1. the 'straight' engine with cylinders placed in line one behind the other;
2. the 'flat' engine with cylinders horizontally opposed to each other, and
3. the 'Vee' engine' in which two rows of cylinders are placed at an angle to each other, in the shape of a letter 'V'.

The diesel engine

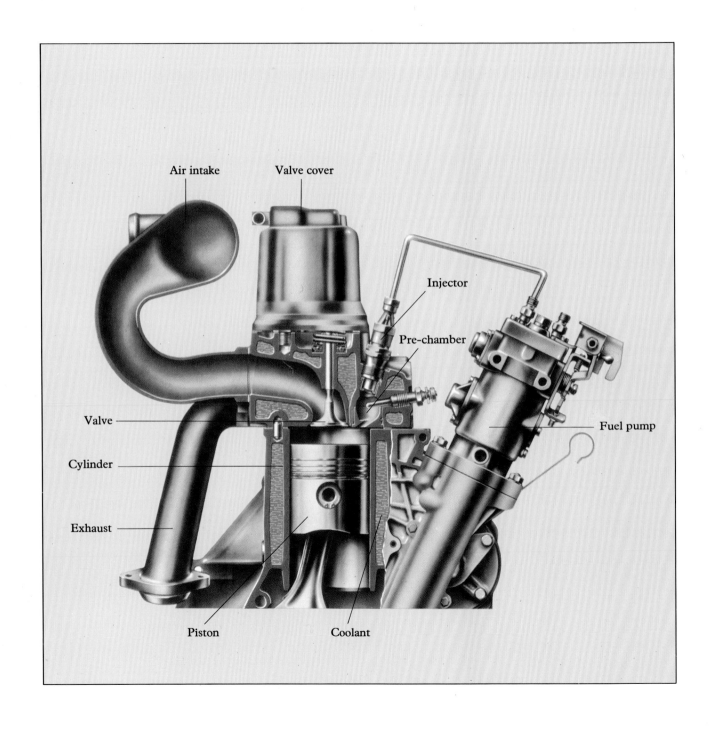

Air intake

Valve cover

Injector

Pre-chamber

Valve

Cylinder

Fuel pump

Exhaust

Piston

Coolant

Apart from the petrol engine there is another type of engine that is also used in cars: the diesel engine.

A diesel engine looks very much the same as a petrol engine, but has some essential differences owing to the fact that it uses a different fuel: derv, whose specific properties we shall look at later on in this book.

A diesel engine also has cylinders, pistons and valves, but differs from the petrol engine in the manner in which the fuel is burned.

While in a petrol engine a mixture of air and petrol vapour is compressed and then ignited by means of a spark, in the diesel engine only air is compressed in the cylinder.

The pressure is much greater however, and so the temperature of the compressed air rises much higher. As the piston reaches its uppermost point, a small amount of diesel fuel is squirted (or injected) into the cylinder where the enormously high temperature ignites it spontaneously. From that moment on, the process is exactly the same as in a petrol engine: the burned gases quickly expand, pushing the piston back down the cylinder.

It will be seen from this that a diesel engine has no need of a coil, distributor or sparking plugs to make a spark. Nor is there any need for a carburettor, since fuel and air only come together in the cylinder and do not have to be mixed first. Instead, diesel engines have ingenious fuel injection systems that provide the cylinders with a small dose of fuel at just the right moment. The most important parts of such systems are the injectors which 'squirt' the fuel into the cylinder, and the fuel pump that keeps the injectors supplied with a carefully metered amount of diesel fuel.

Injector and fuel pump

In a diesel engine, only air is sucked into the cylinder during the induction stroke. The intake valve then shuts and the air is highly compressed, its temperature increasing enormously. The fact that the compression is much greater than in a petrol engine can be seen from the compression ratio, which is about 20:1 in a diesel engine compared with about 8:1 in a petrol engine. When the piston is almost at its highest point an amount of diesel fuel is injected into the cylinder and, as we have already said, this spontaneously ignites in the high-temperature air.

The place at which the fuel is injected into the cylinder varies from engine to engine; in some engines the fuel comes into the cylinder directly (direct injection) but most car diesel engines have the injector in a separate ante-chamber or pre-combustion chamber. The combustion process starts in this chamber, the expansion of the burning gases forcing the rest of the fuel into the main combustion chamber where it is fully ignited.

35

The injectors are highly accurate precision instruments which 'squirt' a minute but carefully metered amount of fuel into the cylinder. The diesel fuel also has to be injected at great force to overcome the huge pressure inside the cylinder, and also because there is not even a hundredth of a second available for injection and combustion.

The metering and forced supply of the fuel is carried out by the fuel pump which is usually mounted alongside the engine itself. There are as many pump elements as there are cylinders, and the pump is driven by the camshaft.

The fuel pump is the most vulnerable part of the diesel engine: each of its components must be manufactured with the utmost precision in order to cope with the very tiny quantities of fuel at very high pressures. The fuel is filtered several times before it reaches the pump, since even the smallest particle of dirt might damage the pump and render it useless.

Diesel or petrol engine

Comparing a diesel with a petrol engine as the best source of propulsion for a passenger car is a tricky business. Both types of engine have their advantages and drawbacks which may or may not be important, depending on the motorist's circumstances and how

he drives. Let us look at some of the main ones.

To begin with, the diesel engine is clearly better in terms of energy utilisation. As the illustration opposite shows, the diesel engine converts approx. 32% of the energy stored in the fuel into mechanical (rotational) energy, while the petrol engine makes use of a maximum of only 24%. The rest of the potential energy is lost as useless heat through the exhaust system and cooling system, and as radiant heat loss. Hence the diesel engine is environmentally kinder, as explained in a later chapter entitled 'Fuels and the environment'.

The diesel engine involves greater production costs, on the other hand. As a general guideline, a diesel engine is about twice the price of a petrol engine of the same power, the reason being that the diesel engine's much greater compression necessitates a really tough construction together with the use of highly sensitive, and thus costly, injection equipment.

In terms of performance, the petrol engine clearly has the edge over the diesel engine, and to achieve a certain power output the diesel engine must have a greater internal volume – in effect, be a bigger engine – than the comparable petrol unit. This is because its heavier construction restricts its maximum engine speed.

As regards maintenance costs, the two kinds of engine do not differ very much: the diesel engine's sturdy

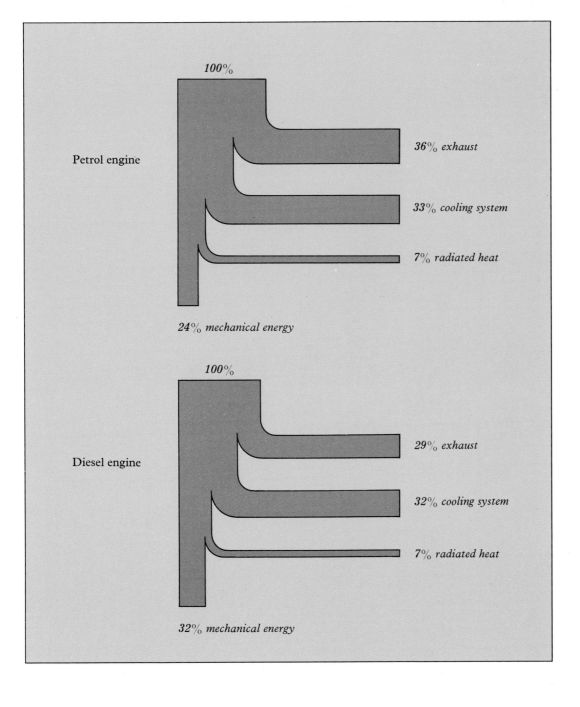

Petrol engine

100%

36% exhaust

33% cooling system

7% radiated heat

24% mechanical energy

Diesel engine

100%

29% exhaust

32% cooling system

7% radiated heat

32% mechanical energy

construction and lack of electrical ignition system make it more reliable; but repairs, when needed, are more expensive.

The biggest difference, so far as the average motorist is concerned, is the lower running cost of a diesel car.

Derv – the fuel used for a diesel engine – is generally cheaper than petrol, and in some countries this difference is made much greater by heavier tax on petrol than on derv. Examples are France and Italy. Differences in fuel prices are, of course, liable to change, but the diesel-powered car scores with consistently better fuel consumption – often up to 50 per cent more miles per gallon – than the equivalent model, driven at the same speeds, and powered by a petrol engine. Motorists who cover a lot of mileage in the course of a year can save on travel costs in spite of higher prices for the diesel version instead of the equivalent petrol model. At the time of writing, Britain's annual car tax is the same whether the engine is petrol or diesel.

Transmission, suspension, steering and brakes

The transmission

The clutch

Gears – the basic principles

The gearbox

Automatic transmission

Continuously variable transmission

The propeller shaft

Final drive, differential and rear axle

The suspension system

The steering system

The brakes

This layout is for a left-hand drive vehicle

Gearbox

Propeller shaft

Final drive

The transmission

In motor engineering, 'transmission' covers all mechanisms which transmit the engine's rotary motion to the road wheels.

This sounds simpler than is in fact the case, since in addition to the job of transmitting the rotary motion of the engine, i.e. of the crankshaft, to the road wheels, the transmission also has to change the direction and relative speed of that motion.

The self-same problems are to be found in an ordinary bicycle: the place where the motion is required, i.e. at the back wheel, is not the same as the place where the motion is created, i.e. the pedals. The direction may be the same but the speed is not: if the back wheel could only turn as fast as you can pedal, you would not make very fast progress. In a bicycle, this problem is solved by the chain and chainwheels. The chain transmits the motion, and since the chainwheel on the pedals is bigger than the one on the back wheel the turning motion is speeded up to enable you to cycle quite fast with some brisk pedalling.

In a car, the problem of transmitting the motion is fairly easy to solve. Most cars have the engine at the front, which drives the rear wheels, and the engine's motion is carried from the front to the back of the car by means of a long shaft, the propeller shaft, which is linked to the crankshaft.

The problem of speed is the opposite from that in a bicycle. In a bicycle the wheel turns faster than the pedals, but in a car the engine always rotates faster than the road wheels, the reason being that in order to make the car travel at a certain speed the engine has to turn more frequently, otherwise it will just not develop the necessary power.

In modern cars the ratio of the crankshaft speed to that of the wheels (in top gear) is around 3.5:1, in other words if the engine is rotating 3500 times per minute, the road wheels will turn only 1000 times during the same period. With an average size wheel this converts to a road speed of about 60 mph, although this varies from car to car.

In a car, the effective speed of the crankshaft is reduced by means of a set of gears which are located between the driven road wheels and which together form the final drive which passes on the motion from the propeller shaft which we mentioned earlier, to the wheels. At the same time the direction of the motion is changed, as we shall see later.

Now the propeller shaft and final drive together would form a complete transmission system if the car maintained a constant speed at all times. However, the car has to be able to move off from a standstill, climb steep hills, etc., and greater pulling power is needed for such operations.

The pulling power of an engine is largely dependent upon its speed of rotation, as we have already seen. The faster the crankshaft turns, the more power is developed and the average engine generates its maximum power at about 75 per cent of its maximum speed. When the car is travelling slowly and the engine has to develop a lot of tractive effort (for accelerating, for instance), the effective speed of the crankshaft has to be increased in relation to the speed at which the driven wheels turn.

This job is done by the car's gearbox, in which a number of gear combinations are able to reduce the turning speed of the propeller shaft in relation to the crankshaft. Each combination has a different degree of reduction with the result that the car's whole speed range is covered. In addition the gearbox makes it possible to isolate the engine from the propeller shaft and final drive altogether, so that the engine can turn without the road wheels moving.

In order for the gearbox itself to be operated (by the driver) it has to be possible to isolate it from the engine as well. If the car is stationary and the engine is running, there has to be a progressive type of connection to allow the car to move off smoothly and without jolts. The same applies to changing from one gear combination to another, and so all cars with a manual gearbox (i.e., *not* automatic) have a clutch mechanism.

The transmission system is now complete as far as the final drive, and the motion of the engine could be transmitted to the road wheels were it not for the fact that the two driven road wheels do not always turn at the same speed. As the car turns a corner, for example, the wheel on the outside of the turn has to cover a greater distance and so must turn faster than the wheel on the inside. Ths is made possible by the differential, a set of gears built into the final drive. The entire transmission system is rounded off by two shafts running from the differential to the wheels.

Of course, transmission systems can also vary, since the arrangement of engine and driven wheels changes from car to car. When the car has its engine at the back driving the back wheels, then the differential can be combined with the gearbox. The same applies in front-engined cars with front-wheel drive.

For the sake of simplicity and clarity however we shall confine our description to the traditional layout with the engine at the front and the driven wheels at the back, with brief reference to the more important variations.

There is also a difference in the extent to which the motorist has to operate the transmission. With non-automatic (manual) transmission he has to operate the system himself, while automatic or semi-automatic transmissions do all or part of the work for him.

The clutch

The clutch, a permanent feature of non-automatic transmissions, does two things. First, it allows the driver to interrupt the connection between engine and gearbox so that he can change gear. Second, the clutch makes sure that re-connection of engine and gearbox after a gear change is smooth and gradual. The clutch is therefore located between the engine and gearbox, or to be precise, against the engine's flywheel.

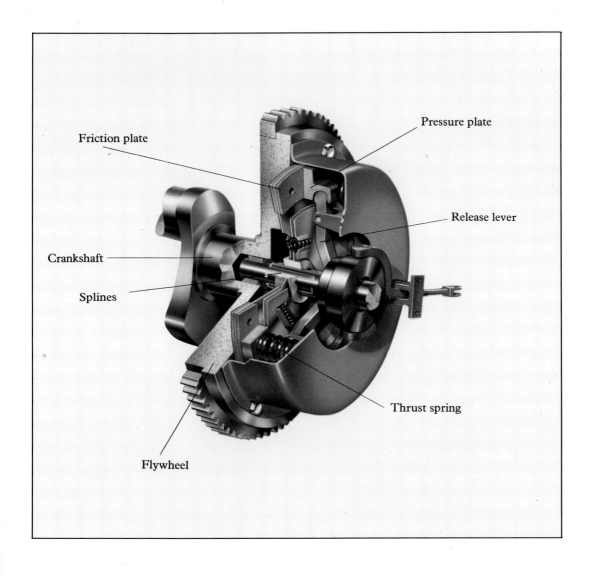

Friction plate

Pressure plate

Release lever

Crankshaft

Splines

Thrust spring

Flywheel

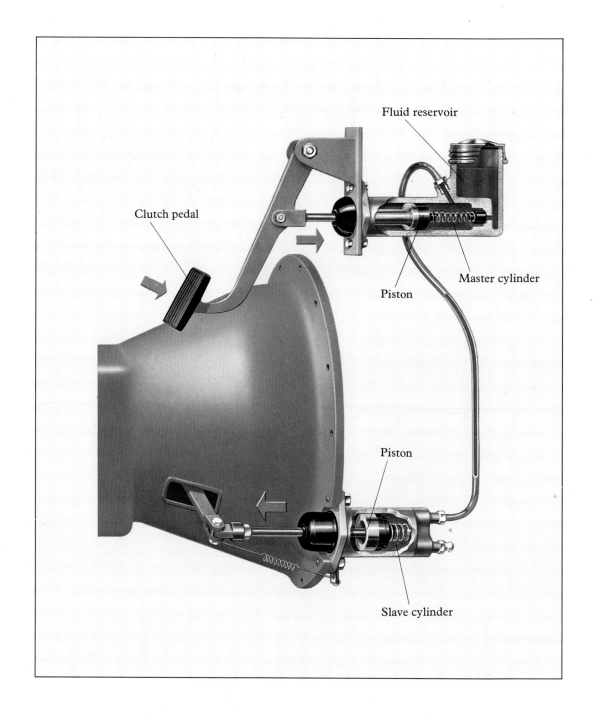

Fluid reservoir

Clutch pedal

Piston

Master cylinder

Piston

Slave cylinder

The most important part of the clutch is the friction or clutch plate, a round disc faced on both sides, which offers high frictional resistance but is not affected by heat and does not wear out quickly. The disc is fitted to the input shaft of the gearbox so that it is able to rotate with it but is also free to slide along it, a method of fixing known as 'splined'. As long as the clutch pedal is not depressed, the clutch plate is pressed against the flywheel by the pressure plate. The force with which the pressure plate is pressed against the clutch plate is provided by a number of powerful springs. The frictional resistance of the plate ensures that the flywheel turns the clutch plate with the result that the rotary motion of the engine is transmitted along to the gearbox.

During a gear change, the pressure plate is pulled back against the pressure of the springs so that the clutch plate can move away from the flywheel. This is accomplished by means of a number of levers, the release levers, which can be operated by means of a simple hydraulic or mechanical system.

The clutch pedal inside the car is connected to the piston of a so-called master cylinder that is filled with a special fluid contained in a reservoir. When the pedal is pressed down, this fluid is pressed from the master cylinder along a pipe to a slave cylinder and moves its piston, which operates the pressure plate.

When the clutch pedal is released again, the springs take over and press the pressure plate back against the clutch plate which is thus held firmly against the flywheel. How it all actually works can be readily grasped as the car moves away from standstill. The engine is turning, and with it the flywheel, but the clutch plate is separated from the flywheel and so is motionless. The plate is then slowly pressed against the flywheel and slips against it to begin with; but, as the pressure increases, the plate turns faster and faster until it is turning as fast as the engine, having completed a smooth but positive connection between engine and gearbox. At the same time, the fluid flows from the slave cylinder back to the master cylinder.

An alternative to the hydraulic system is an arrangement of cable and levers that transmit the movement of the clutch pedal mechanically. In addition, the clutch springs can be replaced by a so-called diaphragm spring, a spring steel disc that presses against the whole of the pressure plate.

Gears – the basic principles

We shall be talking a lot about gears in the following sections, and so it is worthwhile just pausing a moment to consider the basic principles on which gears work.

The basic principle is essentially one of leverage.

Levers are used to lift heavy objects with reduced effort. If a lever is placed beneath a weight of 100 Newtons (N), relatively little force is needed to raise it, depending, of course, on where the fulcrum is placed.

In the illustration below for example, the lever is positioned on the fulcrum so that the left-hand section is twice the length of the right-hand section. As a result, a force of only 50 N needs to be exerted on the free end of the lever to lift twice the weight (100 N) at the other end. The same principles apply to gears as well.

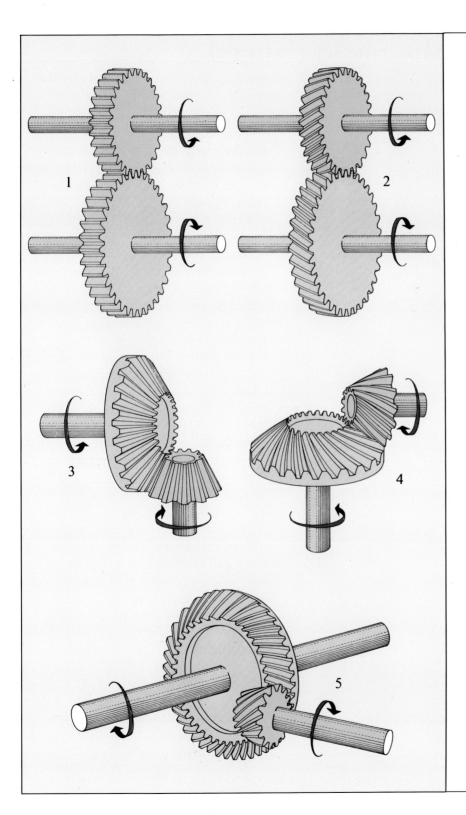

Types of gears
There are many types of gear wheel, but it will be useful to have a look at the types most commonly used in car transmission systems, to which we shall refer later on.

1. Spur gears
In this, the most common of all gear combinations, the teeth run parallel to the shaft on which the wheels turn.

2. Helical gears
These have their teeth cut in a curve so that one end of a tooth meshes with another before the other end has disengaged. These gears run much more quietly.

3 & 4. Bevel and spiral bevel gears
These gears are used when there has to be a change of direction of the drive. Bevel gear teeth are cut straight across a conical wheel, while spiral bevel gears have teeth cut in a curve like helical gears.

5. Hypoid gears
This is a variant of the spiral bevel gear in which the driving shaft runs at a lower level than the driven shaft. They are used in the final drive to allow the car floor above the propeller shaft to be lower.

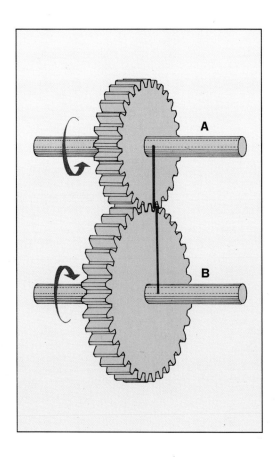

Now let us look at a simple gear. Here we have two gear wheels, the diameter of B being twice that of wheel A. The red lines running from the centres of the wheels to the teeth are imaginary levers. If wheel A is turned or, as we say, torque is applied to its shaft, the short lever will bear against the long lever of wheel B. Because this lever is twice as long as the lever in wheel A, the torque resulting in the shaft of wheel B will be twice that applied to the shaft of wheel A.

Since gear B is twice the size of gear A it will have twice the number of teeth, each of which can be thought of as a lever. As gear A turns, its teeth push round the teeth of gear B in the opposite direction, but because of the difference in the number of teeth, gear B will rotate only half a turn for every complete turn of gear A, and hence at half the speed. The relationship between the number of teeth which mesh with one another is called the 'gear ratio' and in this particular example the ratio is 2:1 since one gear has twice as many teeth as the other.

Gears can therefore be used to do two main jobs: multiply the torque produced by the engine and alter the speed relationship. They can also be used to reverse the direction of rotation of the drive or to alter the angle of the driven shaft in relation to that of the driving shaft.

The gearbox

As we have already seen, in certain circumstances (like travelling slowly or climbing hills) the engine has to turn fast to produce the necessary power, while the road wheels are turning slowly. An arrangement of gears – called the gearbox – provides the choice of gears to suit the conditions.

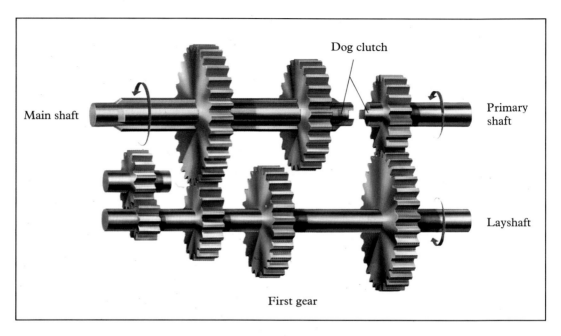

Dog clutch

Main shaft

Primary shaft

Layshaft

First gear

The gearbox has a number of gear wheel combinations, called simply 'gears', which can be varied according to circumstance. We can see how this works in practice by looking at a simple three-speed (i.e. three forward gears) gearbox.

The turning motion of the engine is transmitted to the primary shaft of the gearbox via the clutch. In line with the primary shaft, but quite separate from it, is the propeller shaft which is ultimately connected to the road wheels. A second shaft lies parallel to the primary and propeller shafts, and this one is called the layshaft.

On the primary shaft is a gear wheel which is permanently in mesh with a bigger gear wheel on the layshaft. Further to the left on the layshaft are

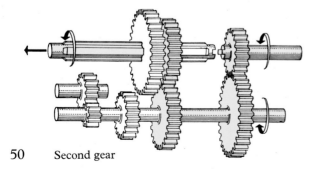

Second gear

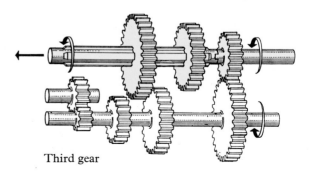

Third gear

gear wheels for first and second gear and for reverse gear as well. On the propeller shaft there are two gear wheels which are 'splined' to the shaft so that they can slide along the shaft while turning with it all the time.

As the engine turns, its motion is transmitted via the primary shaft to the gear wheels on the layshaft. If we now slide one of the gear wheels on the propeller shaft so that it meshes with a gear wheel on the layshaft, the motion is transmitted through to the road wheels.

The illustration opposite above shows first gear engaged. If we now suppose that the gear wheel on the primary shaft is half the size of that on the layshaft, it becomes clear that the layshaft will only turn half as fast as the primary. If the meshing gear wheels on the layshaft and propeller shaft also have the same ratio of size, then the propeller shaft will in all turn four times slower than the primary shaft, and the gear ratio is 4:1.

As second gear is engaged, the two gear wheels on the propeller shaft slide such that the wheel of first gear disengages and the second gear wheel meshes with the corresponding gear wheel on the layshaft. If these two gear wheels are the same size, the overall gear ratio will be reduced to 2:1, since only the gear wheel combination between primary shaft and layshaft will cause any reduction.

In third gear, which is actually top gear in our example, the primary shaft is directly connected to the propeller shaft by means of a 'dog clutch'. All the gear wheels in the gearbox actually turn without doing anything, since the motion of the engine is transmitted without any reduction. In other words the gear ratio is 1:1, or direct.

So far, the propeller shaft has been turning in the same direction as the primary shaft, but if we want the car to reverse, it has to be possible to reverse this turning motion as well. In reverse gear, therefore, we use a reverse 'idler' which can be moved between two gear wheels on the layshaft and propeller shaft respectively.

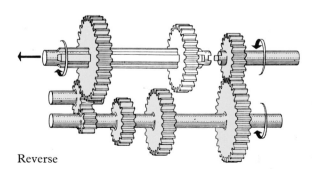

Reverse

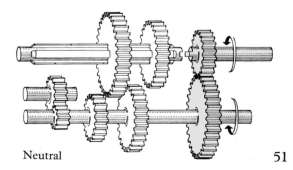

Neutral

Finally, the gearbox can be in 'neutral', which means that the layshaft turns but not the propeller shaft, so that the engine can run with the car at rest and the clutch engaged.

Of course, modern gearboxes are much more complicated than we have just described. The box still contains a number of gear wheel pairs for the various gears, but a few ingenious devices have been added to make gear-changing easier.

With the old-fashioned gearbox, the driver had to bring pairs of gears to the same speed before they could be engaged, a difficult operation requiring considerable skill and which was often noisy. Nowadays, gears which are constantly in mesh are used (the 'constant-mesh' system). To achieve this, the gear wheels are fixed to the propeller shaft in such a way that they are free to turn on it. As soon as a gear is engaged, the appropriate gear wheel

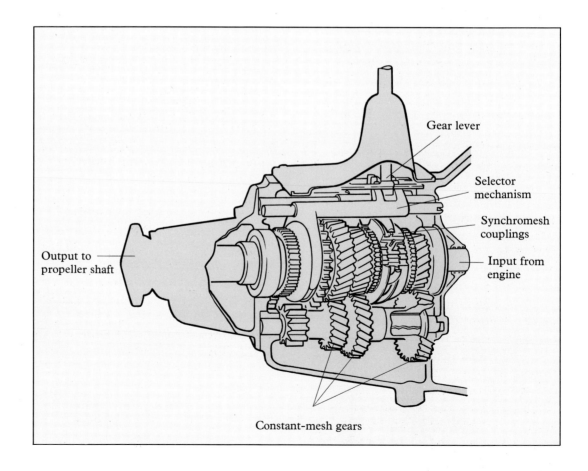

Gear lever

Selector mechanism

Synchromesh couplings

Input from engine

Output to propeller shaft

Constant-mesh gears

52

is locked on the propeller shaft so that the motion can be transmitted.

To make gear-changing as smooth as possible, the gear wheel is not locked on the propeller shaft suddenly, but gradually. This is done by means of the synchromesh device which ensures that the gear wheel and propeller shaft reach the same speed (i.e. are synchronised) before they are locked together.

Another benefit of the constant-mesh system is that it uses gear wheels with curved teeth, making for a much quieter gearbox.

As a rule the constant-mesh system is used only for the forward gears, while for reverse gear – and sometimes for first gear too – gear wheels are used which slide into each other (sliding mesh).

The gear wheels and the necessary changing mechanisms are housed inside the gearbox which is usually mounted, together with the clutch, immediately behind the engine. The box is operated by a 'stick' mounted on top of it or by a gear lever on the steering column. In modern cars the three-speed gearbox in our simplified example is not used any more. A larger number of gears – four or five – means that better use can be made of the engine's power.

The actual gear ratios are not as 'round' as in our examples. With the 2:1 ratio, for instance, the teeth on the small wheel would always meet the same teeth on the large wheel, every two revolutions, and so by making the ratio slightly different, say 2.13:1, we can make sure that different teeth are meshing all the time, thus ensuring that gear wear is far more regular. Another reason is that car engineers try to develop exactly the right gear ratios to suit the engine and the car, regardless of the actual numerical value of the gear ratio that results.

Overdrive

A true overdrive unit is an extra gear combination which, when engaged, makes the propeller shaft turn faster than the crankshaft. At a given speed of, say, 70 mph, the engine of a car with overdrive does not have to turn as fast as the engine of the same car without overdrive. This saves fuel and reduces unnecessary engine wear, as well as making the car quieter at speed. Its advantage is that it has its own 'clutch', and is simply engaged or disengaged just by an electric switch. Power to the wheels is sustained during the change into or out of overdrive.

Manufacturers sometimes claim that their cars have an 'overdrive' top gear; this gives the desired impression, but unless a separate overdrive unit is fitted, it is a misuse of the term.

Automatic transmission

The automatic gearbox has a number of obvious advantages. The driver does not need to operate the clutch and change gear by hand; less physical and mental effort is called for and the driver can concentrate fully on steering, accelerating and braking.

Instead of the gear lever, with its complex movements in two or three planes, the automatic has a selector lever which moves in just one plane. Its positions are usually marked P-R-N-D-2-1, and some of the positions such as P (Park) and R (Reverse) are safeguarded by notches, so that they are not selected in error. They can be selected only when the driver means to do so, and works a positive release catch to clear the notch. With the engine running, and D (Drive) selected, simply pressing the accelerator pedal starts the car moving, and normally thereafter all gears are changed up or down automatically depending on the road speed and the position of the accelerator. By always changing gear at just the right moment, a car with automatic transmission should run more economically than a car with manual gear change. In practice,

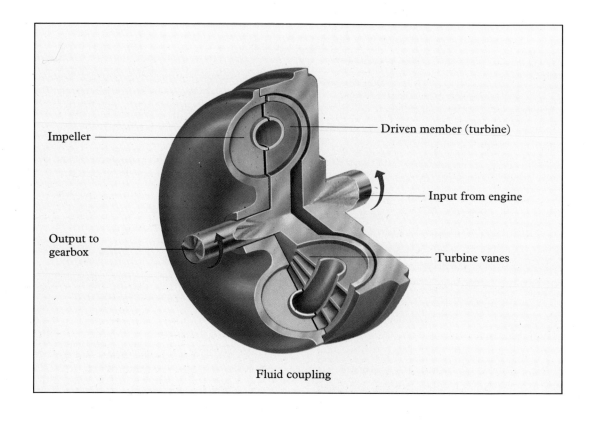

Impeller — Driven member (turbine)

Input from engine

Output to gearbox — Turbine vanes

Fluid coupling

however, the automatic selection is often less well timed than that of a skilled driver; in addition, slip takes place in the torque converter which has the effect that an automatic car usually consumes more fuel than its manual equivalent.

The automatic gearbox is a highly complex piece of machinery, but for our purposes a description of the fundamental principles will be quite adequate. Basically it consists of a torque converter and a number of 'planetary' gears, plus the necessary control mechanisms.

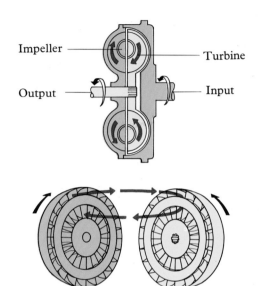

The torque converter

As we have seen, the manually operated gearbox has a clutch to ensure that the connection with the engine can be smoothly interrupted and re-established. The 'torque' does not change and is merely adapted to suit driving conditions on a step-by-step basis (changing up or down through the gears).

On an automatic gearbox this job is partly done by a torque converter which not only transmits the engine's motion, allowing the car to move away smoothly from rest, but also multiplies the torque of the engine at low road speeds. We can see how it works with the aid of a simple fluid clutch, from which the torque converter has been developed.

The fluid clutch consists of two 'wheels' – the impeller, which is driven by the engine, and the turbine, which is connected to the gearbox. The impeller also forms a casing and is attached to the engine crankshaft. Both wheels have a number of radial vanes so that they can be compared with two halves of a grapefruit with the fruit scooped out. The wheels are fitted so that they can turn freely one from the other, and the whole unit is filled with oil.

With rotation of the engine and the impeller, the oil in the torque converter is thrown by centrifugal force towards the outer part of the wheel and forced between the vanes of the turbine. As the engine turns faster, the force acting on the turbine increases and when sufficient torque is transmitted, this force begins to make the turbine rotate

55

as well. The fluid in the turbine flows towards the centre and then returns to the impeller which again increases its momentum. The fluid continues to circulate as long as the impeller turns faster than the turbine, which is always the case.

Thus the fluid clutch transmits power from the engine to the gearbox, although always with a certain power loss. When the engine is idling, the fluid force is not great enough to rotate the turbine, with the result that the engine is virtually disconnected from the gearbox. As the engine is accel-

erated, the torque increases and the drive is taken up smoothly.

The actual torque converter itself has one extra component than the fluid clutch, as the illustration below shows. There is a stator between the impeller and the turbine – the stator is a vaned wheel. When the impeller is rotated by the engine, the fluid flows from its vanes to the turbine vanes, passing outside the stator. In returning from the turbine to the impeller it passes through the stator. The stator's vanes propel the fluid with increased energy, via the impeller, back to the turbine.

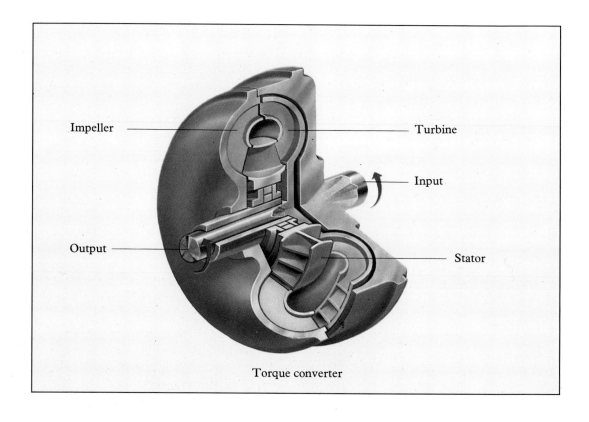

Impeller — Turbine

Input

Output — Stator

Torque converter

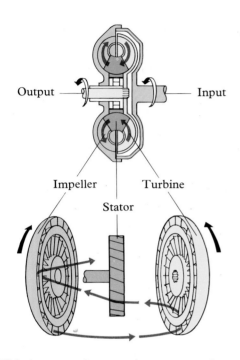

Output — Input

Impeller — Turbine

Stator

This increased power is greatest when the engine is running fast and the car is stationary, in other words when moving off, so that maximum torque is transmitted to the road wheels to set the car in motion.

The epicyclic gearbox

In the manual gearbox we saw how the 'usual' gear combinations are changed to suit various speeds. In the automatic gearbox, however, so-called epicyclic (or planetary) gears are used which have more combination possibilities and are also better suited to automatic operation.

In an epicyclic set of gears the gear wheels do not just rotate on a shaft; they also rotate bodily around the axis of the complete gear wheel set. The principle is clearly shown below.

In the centre of the set is the sun gear (yellow) around which the planetary gears (blue) rotate; the planetary gears have their own axes about which they are able to turn. The whole system is held together by the ring gear, an outer internally-toothed wheel, with which the planetary gears mesh.

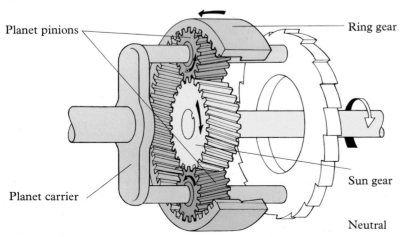

Planet pinions — Ring gear

Sun gear

Planet carrier

Neutral

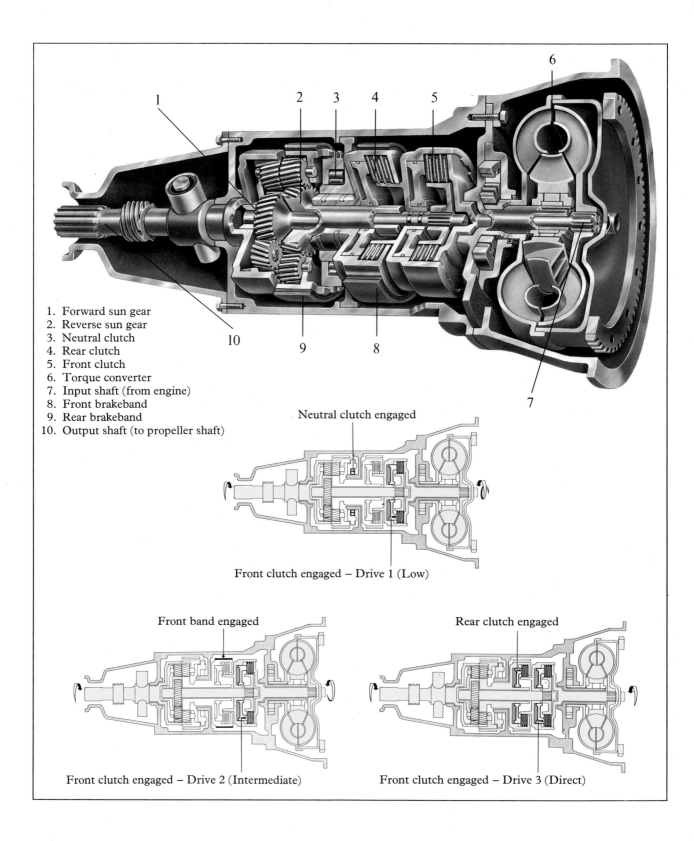

1. Forward sun gear
2. Reverse sun gear
3. Neutral clutch
4. Rear clutch
5. Front clutch
6. Torque converter
7. Input shaft (from engine)
8. Front brakeband
9. Rear brakeband
10. Output shaft (to propeller shaft)

Neutral clutch engaged

Front clutch engaged – Drive 1 (Low)

Front band engaged

Front clutch engaged – Drive 2 (Intermediate)

Rear clutch engaged

Front clutch engaged – Drive 3 (Direct)

If we assume that the sun gear is connected to the engine and the planet carrier is connected to the car's road wheels, then the entire system has the following three possibilities:

1. Neutral. The sun gear is driven, while the planet carrier stays still. The planetary gears rotate about their own axes, taking the ring gear with them which is free to rotate.
2. Reduction. The sun gear is driven, but the ring gear is held fast by a brake band. The planetary gears are thus forced to roll round in the ring gear, turning their carrier in the same direction of rotation, but at a slower speed.
3. Direct Drive. The sun gear is driven and is locked together with the ring gear at the same time. The planetary gears are unable to rotate and their carrier is forced to rotate with the sun gear in the same direction and at the same speed.

Reversing is also possible: drive is taken from the ring gear, and the planet carrier is locked fast. The sun gear then drives the planetary gears, which in turn drive the ring gear making it rotate more slowly and in the opposite direction.

These are the basic essentials of the automatic gearbox – obviously the actual equipment is much more complex, comprising not one but two or more epicyclic gear sets in which the various gear wheels can be interconnected by a number of plate clutches and brake bands.

The whole transmission unit is operated by an involved hydraulic system which regulates the selection of gears to suit the effort being demanded of the car – hill climbing, accelerating, and so on – the demand dictated by the driver's foot on the accelerator, and the speed.

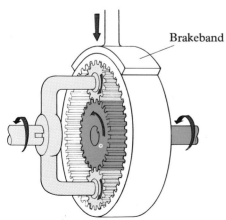

Ring gear locked

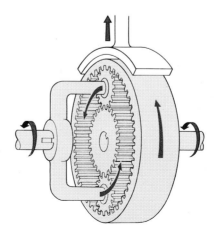

Direct drive

Continuously variable transmission

In addition to the fully automatic gearbox there is yet another transmission system in which there is no changing of gears; this is the 'Variomatic System' developed in the Netherlands, and is currently known by the abbreviation CVT (continuously variable transmission). With CVT, the rotation of the engine is not reduced by fixed gear wheel combinations but by an ingenious system of Vee-belts and belt pulleys.

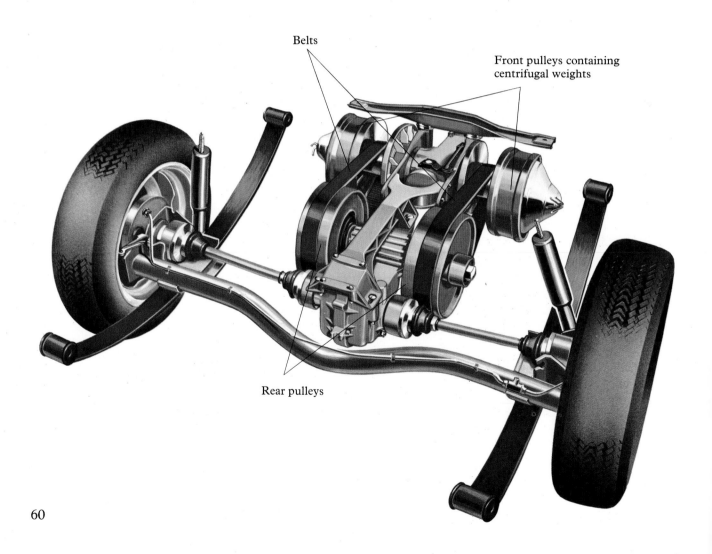

Belts

Front pulleys containing
centrifugal weights

Rear pulleys

The illustration shows that the CVT system consists of two belt drives. The forward belt pulleys are driven by the engine via the propeller shaft and an angled gear, while the rear pulleys are connected via a set of gear wheels to the road wheels.

The ingenious part of the system is that the belt pulleys change their effective size. Each pulley in fact consists of two halves, one of which is movable. When this half is pressed against the other half the belt is pushed outwards and the pulley is at its greatest diameter.

When the pulleys are pulled apart from each other however, the belt 'sags' between the two halves and turns on a smaller diameter.

When the engine is running slowly the halves of the forward pulleys are far apart; the rear pulley halves are pressed against each other by a spring with the result that transmission passes from a small to a larger diameter, i.e. the engine rotation is effectively 'geared down', as required for starting from rest and climbing steep hills.

As soon as the engine starts to turn faster, two centrifugal weights inside the forward pulleys come into action. Centrifugal force throws the weight outward, and because they are hinged, the movable part of the forward pulley is pressed against the fixed half with the result that the belt is pushed outward. The belt of course has a fixed length and does not stretch so that the halves of the rear pulleys are forced outward against the pressure of the spring.

The faster the engine turns, the more the halves of the forward pulleys are forced against each other, and so the reduction process becomes less and less. This means that the rotary speed of the engine is reduced by the right amount at every moment and the best possible use is made of the engine's torque.

In reality the pressing together of the forward belt pulleys is assisted by a control system which makes use of the partial vacuum existing inside the engine's induction manifold. This makes it possible for the reduction to increase again when the driver depresses the accelerator, with an effect similar to 'changing down' in a manual gearbox.

The advantage of the CVT system is that transmission is totally stepless and progressive. One drawback, however, is that the system is less suited for the transmission of relatively high torques, which is one reason why it is used only in small cars. It is also not as smooth in taking up the drive from rest as an automatic transmission with hydraulic torque converter. Nevertheless, the principle of the CVT is being developed for future application in different form.

The propeller shaft

The engine power which the gearbox has adapted to suit driving conditions must now be passed on to the final drive which, as we said before, is located between the driven road wheels.

In the conventional car, i.e. with a front-mounted engine driving the rear wheels, this is done by means of the propeller shaft. Usually, the final drive is firmly attached to the back axle and thus moves up and down in relation to the rest of the car; the propeller shaft is fixed between the gearbox and the final drive, in a special way, to accommodate this movement.

The propeller shaft has a flexible coupling known as a universal joint at each end. The illustration opposite shows that a universal joint consists of two 'yokes' that face each other at right-angles. The two yokes are connected by a crosspiece or 'spider'. In most universal joints the connections between the spider and the yokes are provided with rubber bushes which require no lubrication.

The fact that the connections be-

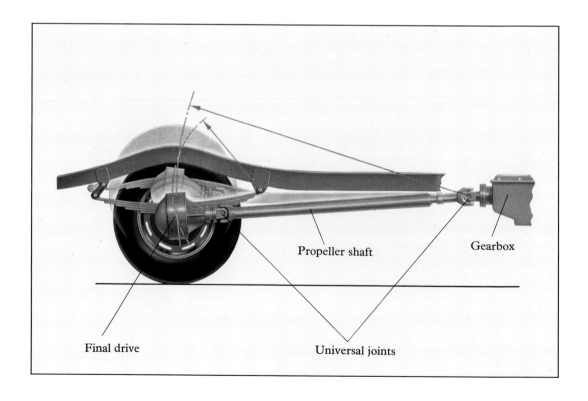

Final drive   Propeller shaft   Universal joints   Gearbox

tween propeller shaft and gearbox and between propeller shaft and final drive are made with universal joints means that the rotating propeller shaft is able to move smoothly up and down at the same time.

Because the vertical movement of the car's wheels, allowed by its suspension, also alters the distance between gearbox and final drive, the propeller shaft is also provided with splines to compensate for this change in length. They fit precisely into a toothed socket, and permit a telescopic effect whenever necessary.

Yokes

Splines

Spider

Final drive, differential and rear axle

Up to now the motion of the engine has always been in the same direction, but in order to be able to drive the road wheels it has to 'turn the corner' and be further reduced, two tasks accomplished by the final drive.

The final drive comprises a set of gear wheels. The smaller wheel, the pinion, is driven by the propeller shaft and is constantly in mesh with the larger crownwheel. These are bevel gears so that the motion is turned through a right-angle. The extent to which the turning speed of the propeller shaft is reduced will depend on the number of teeth on the crownwheel in relation to the number of teeth on the pinion. The final drive might have a typical reduction ratio in the region of 3.5:1, i.e. in top gear (direct drive) the engine turns three-and-a-half times for each turn of the road wheels. In the lower gears, this extent of further reduction still takes place.

Nowadays most final drives have spiral bevel gears that make the transmission almost silent. The so-called hypoid drive is also frequently used; with this, the axis of the pinion is offset from that of the crownwheel, so that the propeller shaft is lowered and the transmission tunnel that runs through the middle of the car can also be at a lower level, as already mentioned on page 47.

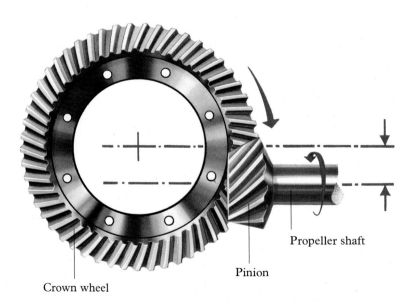

Crown wheel

Pinion

Propeller shaft

Hypoid drive

We said earlier that the two driven road wheels do not always rotate at the same rate. When turning a corner, the wheel on the outside has to cover a greater distance – and hence must turn faster – than the wheel on the inside of the corner. If both wheels were fixed to a single, rigid axle the car would run perfectly well on straight roads, but steering would be extremely difficult and the tyres would soon wear out owing to slippage on corners.

This is why the wheels are mounted on separate axles (half-shafts), both driven by the differential. The differential is fixed to the crownwheel and actually consists of two sets of gears.

One set of gears is attached to the differential 'carrier' that forms a single component with the crownwheel. These gears are able to rotate freely and are engaged with two other gears which are mounted on the half-shafts.

As the engine drives the pinion, the crownwheel rotates taking the differential frame with it. While the car is travelling straight ahead, both road wheels experience equal resistance and the two gears on the ends of the half-shafts rotate at the same speed. The two smaller gears do not turn, and so the whole differential rotates as a solid block.

If one of road wheels experiences more resistance than the other, however, the corresponding gear on the end of the half-shaft will turn more slowly. The crownwheel is still turning as fast as before, on the other hand, and so the two small gears are forced to roll round the slow-turning gear.

In this way, it is possible for the two driven road wheels to turn at different speeds. The amount by which one wheel speeds up is equal to that by which the other slows down, and in the extreme case, when one wheel is forced to stop turning altogether, the other wheel turns twice as fast.

The opposite can also happen, of course. If one of the road wheels feels no resistance at all it will turn twice as fast, while the other will come to a stop. This kind of situation frequently happens with cars that are unable to find grip on slippery surfaces (e.g. snow). To overcome this problem, some cars are provided with a locking differential in which a 'diff-lock' limits the differential action. It ensures that neither wheel can slip excessively. In addition, the final drive and the differential are constructed in such a way that they can be regarded as a single component which is then called the 'back axle'. The differential is often permanently attached to the rear axle housing, creating a rigid unit. The term 'rigid axle' is sometimes wrongly used, but because suspension is always necessary, allowing vertical movement of the axle on bumps, there can never be a rigid axle in a car. The correct term is a 'beam' axle, and one which transmits the engine power to the wheels is a 'live rear axle'. One which just locates the wheels, as in a front-wheel drive car, is a 'dead beam axle'.

65

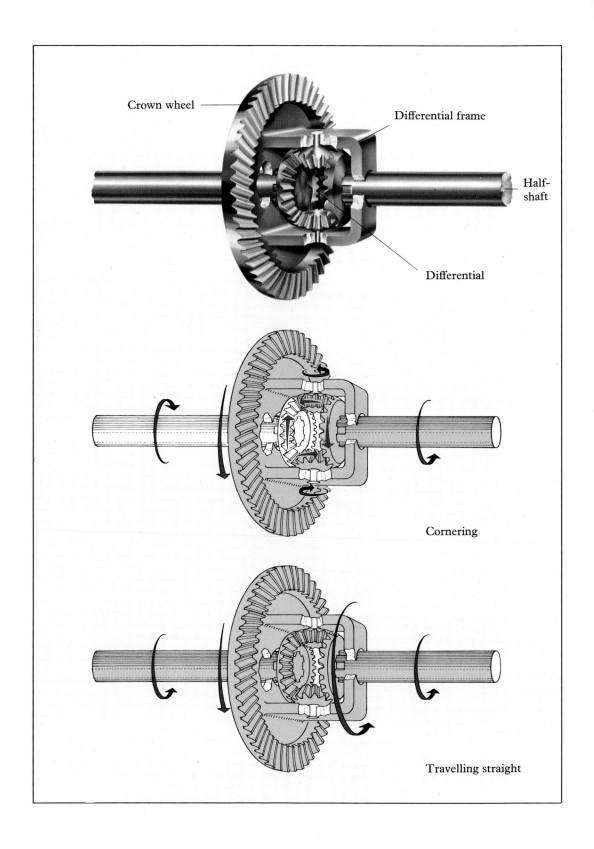

Crown wheel

Differential frame

Half-shaft

Differential

Cornering

Travelling straight

In some cars a different construction is used, in which the differential is attached to the chassis or car body and so cannot move up and down with the wheels. In this case therefore, the drive shafts are provided with universal joints to accommodate the vertical movements allowed by the suspension (see page 68).

mounted, the gearbox may be included inside the engine in place of the usual sump. More usually, though, it is in a separate unit, either on the end of the engine, or behind it.

Other types of final drive

Of course, not all cars have engines at the front driving the rear wheels. Rear-engined cars have no need of a propeller shaft, so the differential is bolted to the gearbox (or may even be inside it) and is thus unable to move up and down with the wheels.

To overcome this difficulty the drive shafts are connected to the differential by means of universal joints, so that they can 'flex'. The same applies when the engine is mounted at the front of the car and drives the front wheels, in which case an extra set of universal joints is required to facilitate the steering of the front wheels. Yet another construction is used when the engine is mounted transversely. There is no need for right-angle drive, hence no necessity for a crownwheel and pinion, which are replaced by, for example, a set of helical gears, one of which carries the differential. In addition, when the engine is transversely

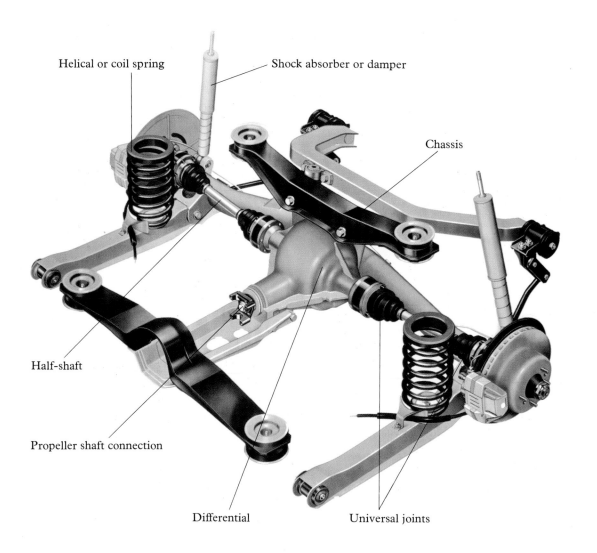

Helical or coil spring

Shock absorber or damper

Chassis

Half-shaft

Propeller shaft connection

Differential

Universal joints

Example: independent rear suspension

The suspension system

Even while travelling on a reasonably good road, a car is exposed to three types of movement which can be uncomfortable for its occupants: bounce, roll and pitch. When the car is travelling at speed, a wheel striking a bump can bounce right off the road and may continue to do so, like a rubber ball that has been thrown down hard. Roll, which is felt most when cornering, is the result of centrifugal force pulling the car body away from the centre of the curve. Pitch occurs when the rear wheels pass over a bump which has already been negotiated by the front wheels. The front of the car drops as the back rises, and the car tends to continue to pitch fore and aft.

Ideally the suspension system should ensure that all these movements are controlled and that the body of the car should travel level, even over an irregular road surface. It is important here that the 'unsuspended mass', i.e. the total mass of all parts which move when the wheels move, is as small as possible, because if the unsuspended mass is great then the 'blow' received by the car body as the wheels run over an irregularity will also be great.

Springs

There are three typical kinds of spring – the leaf spring, the coil or helical spring, and the torsion bar.

The leaf spring consists of a pack of steel strips (the leaves) placed one above the other. This stack is fixed in the middle to an axle and at the ends to the chassis. Each end of the spring is pivoted, and one end is attached by a shackle, a method of attachment which allows for the spring to flex and compensates for the fact that the distance between the two ends increases as the spring straightens out. As the wheel passes over a bump, the spring is compressed and the leaves slide over each other; this creates a tension in the spring which presses the wheel back against the road.

Because leaf springs are quite heavy, and considerably increase the unsuspended mass, they are not used very much in modern cars; their place is taken by the coil spring, which is lighter and usually more flexible.

Sometimes a torsion bar is used; this is simply a rod which is anchored at one end and twisted by the upward movement of the wheel. In untwisting, it forces the wheel back down again.

There are other types of spring as well, such as the rubber cone which can be compressed by the wheel and then expands again. Some cars use inert gases under pressure.

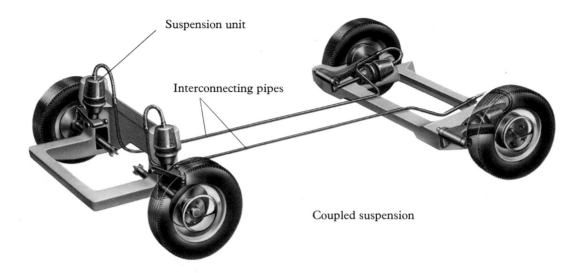

Suspension unit

Interconnecting pipes

Coupled suspension

Shock absorbers

The shock absorber has a function quite different from what this term might suggest. Its job is, in fact, to damp the movement of the spring, restricting its tendency to go on flexing. If there were no shock absorbers, the car would continue to bounce for a long time after going over a bump in the road. As we said, the name is deceptive – the actual shock is absorbed by the springs and tyres, and the more correct term for this unit is 'suspension damper'.

There are many kinds of damper but most work on the hydraulic principle. The absorber consists basically of two telescoping sections which together form a cylinder that is filled with a special fluid. The cylinder contains a piston connected via a rod to the car body and which forces the fluid through a controlled orifice as the two

sections telescope into each other. Since the orifice is small, there is resistance to any rapid movement and the bouncing motion of the spring is damped.

Front suspension

Nowadays, nearly all cars are fitted with independent front suspension, which means that the front wheels are able to move up and down independently of each other. The advantage of this is that the unsuspended mass is kept small and that the wheels have no influence upon each other.

The illustration opposite shows independent front suspension with the shock absorber mounted inside the coil spring – sometimes called concentric. There are similar constructions with a torsion bar each side instead of coil springs.

Rear suspension

Until fairly recently the rear wheels were carried on a live axle which was provided with a leaf spring at either end. However, since the entire rear axle including the differential was part of the unsuspended mass, independent suspension is now often used for the rear wheels too, with either coil springs (see page 68) or torsion bars.

Coupled suspension

In some cars the independent suspensions of front and rear wheels are interconnected by means of a hydraulic system. When one wheel passes over a bump in the road a certain amount of hydraulic fluid is transmitted via pipes and a regulating system to the other wheel on the same side. This helps to ensure that the height and attitude of the car body remain constant.

In addition, most modern cars are fitted with one or two stabiliser bars that connect the suspension on one side to that on the other, at front or rear. These bars prevent the car from leaning over too much on bends, and accordingly they are called anti-roll bars. One anti-roll bar at the front is usual. A few sporting cars have an anti-roll bar at both front and rear.

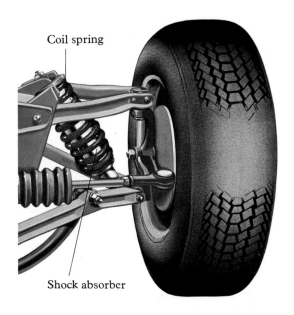

Coil spring

Shock absorber

Independent front suspension

This layout is for a left-hand drive vehicle

Steering wheel

Collapsible steering column

Steering box

Track rod

Ball joints

The steering system

The principle of a car's steering system is basically simple, although the actual construction varies from car to car.

The steering wheel is mounted at the top end of the steering column whose other end is connected to the steering box which has the task of converting the turning motion of the steering wheel into a to-and-fro movement. This to-and-fro movement is then transmitted to the wheels by means of a set of rods, the track rods.

The variations on this theme are essentially concerned with the steering box and the rod mechanism. In the 'worm and peg' steering box, the bottom end of the steering column is provided with an endless screw, the 'worm', in which a conical 'peg' is located. As the steering wheel is turned, the peg moves along the worm and the motion is transmitted to the track rods via a lever or operating arm. Sometimes, to equalise forces on the steering box, a double arm is used, as in the illustration on page 72.

This layout is for a left-hand drive vehicle

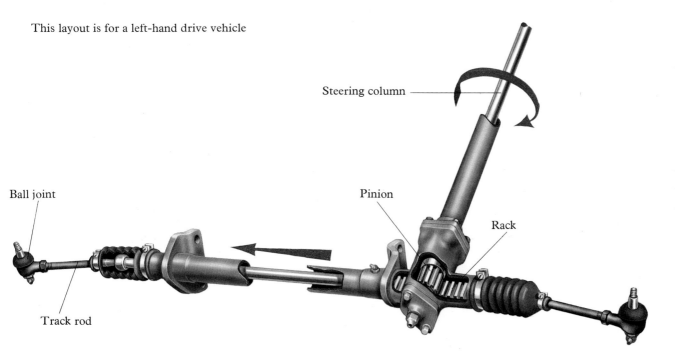

Steering column

Ball joint

Pinion

Rack

Track rod

Rack-and-pinion steering

The 'rack and pinion' system is even simpler, as shown in the illustration below. The bottom end of the steering column is fitted with a gear wheel, known as the pinion, which engages in the teeth of the rack.

As the steering wheel is turned, the rack is moved to the left or right and since the rack is connected to the track rods, the movement is directly transmitted to the wheels. The advantage of this system is the 'directness' of the steering owing to the relatively small number of joints involved. The drawback, however, is that wheel vibration is returned just as directly to the steering wheel and that the steering may feel 'heavy'.

Other types of steering box can also mean heavy steering, which is why some cars, usually the heavier ones, feature hydraulic steering assistance, or power assisted steering.

Power steering does not take the place of the normal mechanical system but merely supplements it to reduce the effort needed to steer a heavy vehicle. That is why the correct term is 'power assisted', not 'power operated'.

The illustrations also show the ball joints, which ensure that the track rod arms can move with the wheels as the latter spring up and down during travel.

The track rod mechanism can vary from the plainly simple to the quite complex. One reason for the increased complexity is the fact that the two front wheels do not have the same degree of 'lock'. The wheel on the inside of a turn, for instance, has to make a smaller circle than the wheel on the outside, and so must lock farther. If this were not the case, then steering would indeed be very heavy and the tyres would wear out very quickly.

The brakes

The job of braking the car, whether to slow it down or stop it altogether, brings us back to the aspect of energy.

In the first chapter we saw how heat generated by the combustion of petrol is converted to 'movement energy' which is needed to make the car move. Most energy is, of course, required to get the car moving at speed, but even when the car is in motion the engine still has to supply energy to overcome the 'rolling resistance' of the tyres on the road and the wind resistance, thus maintaining the speed of the vehicle. When speed is to be decreased, energy has to be removed and this is the task of the brakes.

The brakes use friction to convert the car's movement energy back into heat, thus completing the energy cycle.

There are two types of brake: the drum brake and the disc brake, and most cars are provided with a combination of both kinds. Disc brakes are

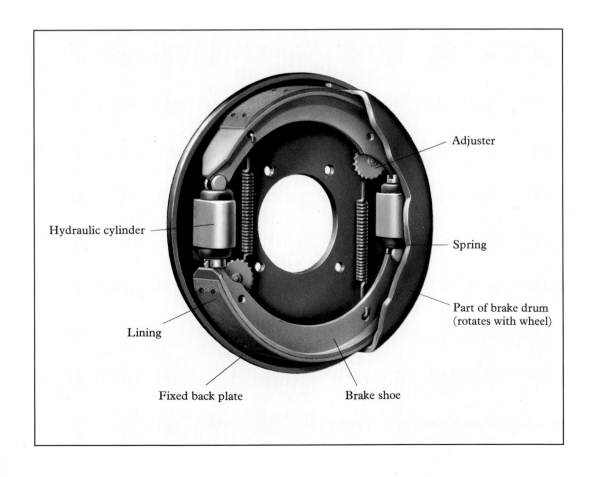

Hydraulic cylinder

Lining

Fixed back plate

Brake shoe

Adjuster

Spring

Part of brake drum (rotates with wheel)

usually used on the front wheels and drum brakes at the rear.

On early cars, brakes used to be operated by cables or rods, but the main drawback of these systems was the difficulty of matching the braking effort left and right. Brakes, when applied, tended to pull the car to one side or the other, so instead all cars now use hydraulics to operate the brakes. The driver's foot on the brake pedal works a piston in a cylinder, forcing fluid to smaller cylinders, one at each wheel, and because hydraulic pressure in a system is equal at any point, the operating effort at each brake is always the same. To safeguard against the possibility of leakage and consequent brake failure, cars now have duplicated hydraulic circuits.

The illustration below shows a dual-circuit brake system. If one of the brake pipes should fail, the brakes at two front and one rear wheel will still operate.

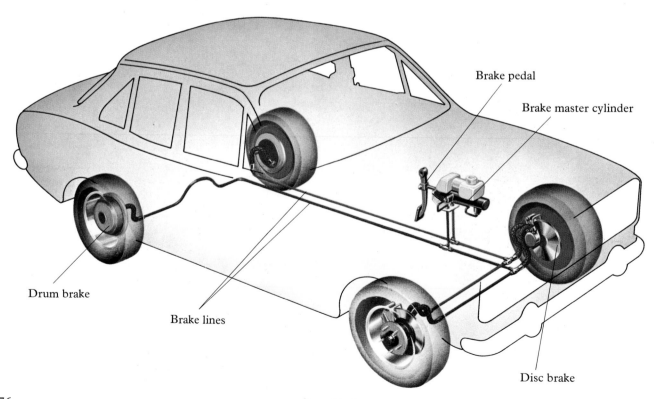

Brake pedal

Brake master cylinder

Drum brake

Brake lines

Disc brake

Car with dual-circuit braking system

Drum brakes

A drum brake consists of two half-moon shaped brake shoes which are mounted on a fixed back plate which cannot rotate with the wheel. Around these shoes is the brake drum, a round metal 'pot' which is attached to the wheel and so rotates with it. When the brake pedal is pressed down with the foot, the brake shoes are pushed outward so that they come into contact with the brake drum. The resulting friction causes the wheel to slow down. The shoes are lined with a special material which can tolerate heat, and has a high friction resistance – the brake lining. When the brake pedal is released, the brake shoes are drawn back from the drum by strong springs.

The pressure on the brake pedal is transmitted to the brake shoes by means of the hydraulic system, comprising a master cylinder and slave cylinders all interconnected by brake pipes. The entire system is filled with brake fluid.

As you press down the brake pedal, the piston in the master cylinder forces the fluid through the brake pipes towards the slave cylinders which are mounted on the back plate between the two brake shoes, and the shoes are pushed outward. Front brakes often have two slave cylinders, one for each brake shoe, which ensure that when you brake, the shoes press more firmly against the drum.

Many cars are also fitted with a brake servo, which reinforces the pedal pressure before passing it on to the wheel cylinders, thus making the brake pedal easier to operate. The energy for the brake servo is usually generated by the vacuum effect created by the engine's induction system (the process of drawing in air to mix with petrol, as explained in the engine section). As the engine runs, it also sucks air from a special chamber called the brake servo. The progressive admission of air to one side of a diaphragm within this servo chamber means that the diaphragm is sucked towards the vacuum side, and this force – the movement of the diaphragm – is used to assist the brake effort. The alternative brake boost method is the use of an engine-driven hydraulic pump.

The hand or parking brake is still mechanically operated, and moves the brake shoes by cables quite independently of the hydraulic system. The hand brake usually acts on the rear wheels only.

Overheating of the brake linings and of the brake drums can cause drum brakes temporarily to lose their efficiency. This phenomenon, called brake fade, does not often happen, but can occur when the brakes are operated often and hard – for instance, when descending a long mountain pass. This is why it is better to change down to a low gear, and use the retarding effect of the engine to hold the car back, instead of keeping steady pressure on the brake pedal.

Disc brakes

The disc brake consists of a steel disc that is fixed to, and so rotates with, the wheel. Either side of the disc are the friction pads which are held in a strong casting, called the calliper. Here again, the pads are activated by the brake cylinders, which are connected to the hydraulic system. As you press down the brake pedal, the pads are pushed against the disc, and the resulting friction slows down the wheel. Advantages of the disc brake are that heat is dissipated more effectively, reducing the risk of fade, and that pull-off springs are not needed.

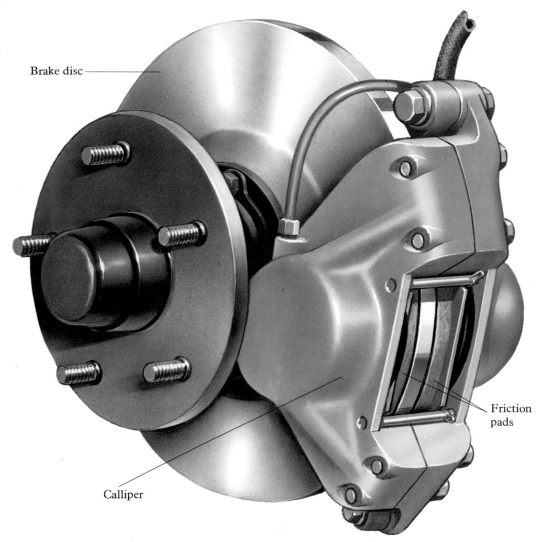

Brake disc

Friction pads

Calliper

Fuels and lubricants

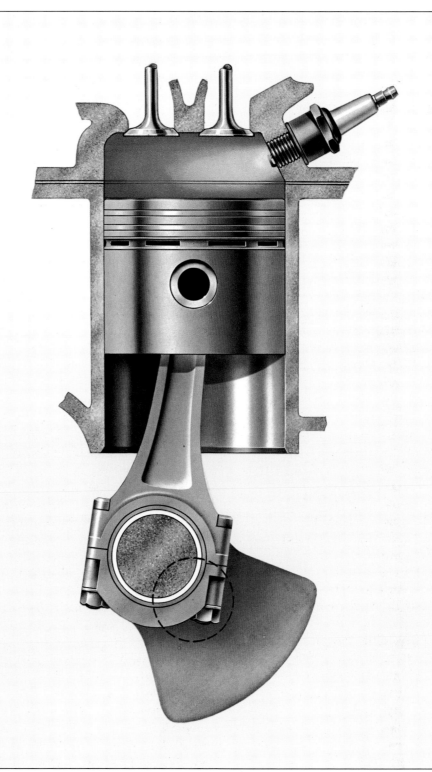

Petrol

A comparison of modern cars with those of fifty or more years ago reveals that the basic principles have not changed all that much, but their practical implementation has been improved.

The very first four-stroke petrol engine, for example, was built in 1886 and today's engines differ little in essence from that early type. Construction has of course been perfected to a large degree, improving the engine's performance and vastly increasing its power. The same thing has also happened to the engine's fuel, petrol. The composition of petrol has remained largely the same but has been developed and perfected by better production methods and the addition of all kinds of special additives. A modern engine would not run very well on the petrol of fifty years ago. However, just as half a century ago, the basis for petrol is still the so-called hydrocarbons: compounds of carbon (C) and hydrogen (H). As it is burned in the engine, the hydrocarbon reacts with the oxygen (O) present in the inducted air, and much heat is released. In the course of this process, the hydrocarbons are converted primarily into carbon dioxide (CO_2) and water vapour (H_2O). For combustion to occur as efficiently as possible, the petrol has to have certain properties which we shall now consider.

Volatility

We make many demands on our cars: the engine must start promptly in both summer and winter, from cold and hot, and reach normal working temperature within a short space of time.

The engine must idle comfortably and speed up smoothly; there must be no vapour locks (see below) in either the fuel pipes or the petrol pump.

All these aspects are affected not only by the construction of the engine but also by the volatility of the petrol. So long as the petrol stays liquid, the hydrocarbon molecules are so close together that the oxygen needed for combustion just cannot 'get past', and so the petrol first has to vaporise before combustion is possible.

One important characteristic of petrol, therefore, is its volatility, i.e. the rate at which it turns to vapour. If volatility is not satisfactory, then too much unvaporised petrol – in the form of tiny droplets – will get into the engine cylinders and combustion will be incomplete. The result of this is not just a loss of power, but also that uncombusted and harmful hydrocarbons will be passed through the exhaust system to the outside air.

The volatility of petrol is dependant upon temperature. As the temperature increases, petrol vaporises more easily, and this is the reason why it is desirable for the engine to reach operating temperature as quickly as possible.

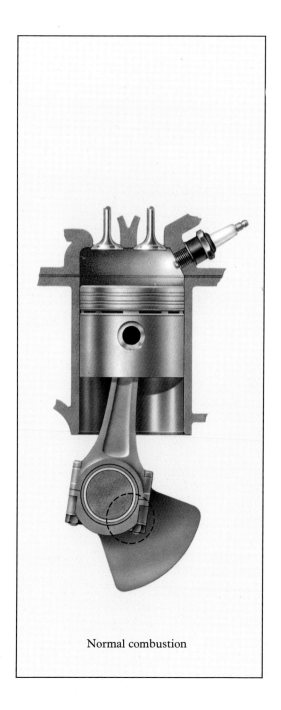

Normal combustion

For the same reason, petrol in temperate climates does not have the same composition in winter as in summer. As the outside temperature drops, the petrol has to vaporise in a 'cold' engine, and so is produced in more volatile form in winter than in summer.

Knock resistance

The mixture of air and petrol vapour which enters the cylinder is ignited by a spark from the sparking plug. Under normal circumstances the mixture should burn very quickly, yet smoothly and evenly. If, however, the compression ratio is too high for the grade of petrol being used, then a part of the mixture burns smoothly when ignited by the spark while the rest ignites spontaneously, causing an explosion which makes the pressure inside the cylinder rise too fast. The result is that the engine knocks or 'pinks', so-called because of the specific noise which this causes.

Engine knock means loss of power and, if it goes on too long, it can cause damage to the engine through local overheating.

Petrol must therefore be resistant to knock and the degree of its knock resistance is indicated by its octane number. The higher the octane number the better the engine's knock resistance.

In Great Britain there are two types of petrol on the market, 2-star and 4-star, each with a particular knock resistance. The octane number of 2-star is around 92; that of 4-star at least 98.

Thus the octane number of petrol is not, as is often supposed, a measure of quality but only of one specific aspect of fuel quality, i.e. resistance to knock. Car manufacturers always state which octane number fuel their cars require; a car manufactured to run on 92 octane petrol will not improve its performance on 98 octane, nor will it be more economical.

The knock resistance of car engines has been vastly improved over the years by better design. In addition, the octane number can be increased by adding lead compounds to the petrol.

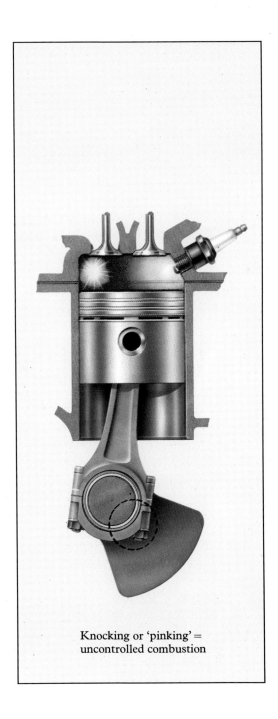

Knocking or 'pinking' = uncontrolled combustion

Additives

There are all kinds of special products which can be added to petrol to combat unwanted side-effects during use. The number and type of these additives, of course, varies from brand to brand, but some have common properties and purposes.

Certain petrols, for example, contain a cleaning additive used to prevent and eliminate impurities in the engine's intake system. Such impurities are chiefly caused by the 'closed crankcase ventilation', a system that has been mandatory for cars in recent years.

In spite of the tight seal created by the piston rings, some combustion gases do pass down the piston into the sump and increase the pressure in it. At one time it was usual to route these gases through a little pipe directly to the outside atmosphere, but today these 'blow-through' gases are returned to the carburettor or the intake manifold. The oil and dirt particles which these gases carry are deposited in the intake system, affecting the air/petrol mixture proportions and eventually increasing the engine's fuel consumption. The cleaning additive in the petrol combats these unwanted deposits.

One additive that most types of petrol contain in winter is the anti-icing additive. As we have already seen, the vaporisation of petrol depends upon heat which is taken from the ambient air. In very low outdoor temperatures the air going into the engine can become so cold that the water vapour in the intake system condenses and freezes, forming a thin layer of ice on the accelerator and carburettor jets. The supply of fuel is impeded and the engine dies. This phenomenon, icing, is prevented by the anti-icing additive.

Most petrols also contain other additives whose job it is, for instance, to prevent loss of fuel quality during long storage periods.

LPG

As odd as it may seem, a petrol engine does not necessarily have to run on petrol. There are other fuels on which petrol engines run well, and one of these is LPG.

LPG – Liquefied Petroleum Gas – is petroleum gas which has been turned into a liquid. The refining of petroleum always releases an amount of gas, consisting mainly of butane and propane, both of which are well known as fuel for industrial and domestic use. LPG is in fact a blend of butane and propane.

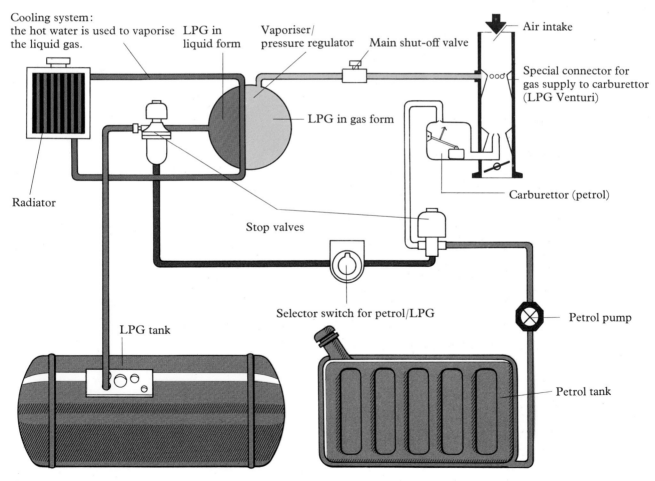

Dual fuel system: switched to LPG

Propane and butane are both hydro-carbons, just like petrol, but with a somewhat different composition. Nevertheless they can be used quite easily for combustion in a petrol engine, and LPG-powered cars are being used in increasing numbers on the roads today.

To make the gas easy to store and handle it is greatly compressed, becoming liquid, with the volume about 250 times smaller. This is why cars that are converted to LPG have to be equipped first with a special installation consisting of a tank in which the gas is kept liquid under great pressure, a device which vaporises the liquid back into gas again, and a special connector for the carburettor.

As a motor fuel, LPG has certain advantages over petrol. For all sorts of reasons the gas burns more completely – hence efficiently – and a car that runs on LPG produces less harmful exhaust gas than a petrol-driven car. LPG is also a 'naturally pure' fuel to which no additivies need be added. (The octane number of LPG is above 100).

Because 1 litre of LPG represents rather less energy than the same quantity of petrol, an LPG-powered engine consumes 15 to 20 per cent more fuel by volume than a petrol engine, while power falls by 5 to 10 per cent at the same time. The attraction of LPG in many countries is its lower price, but this is largely due to lower taxation. In some countries, notably Holland, the price difference in favour of LPG is substantial, but there, LPG cars have to pay more road tax. In Britain, where the overall saving is fairly small, the annual tax rate is the same.

Diesel fuel

As with petrol and LPG, the fuel used for diesel engines consists of hydro-carbons, but of a heavier type, and the fuel is easily recognised by its specific unpleasant smell.

A diesel engine makes quite different demands on its fuel than a petrol engine. While, in a petrol engine, self-ignition has to be prevented as far as possible, in a diesel engine the fuel must ignite spontaneously after injection, but not too fast. This depends, of course, on the so-called self-ignition temperature. The whole process can be described briefly as follows.

The injector administers a stream of finely atomised fuel into the engine cylinder. The tiny droplets of fuel are heated up by the hot surrounding air, boil, and the resulting vapour increases in temperature until the self-ignition temperature is reached, causing spontaneous combustion. The speed at which this process occurs will also depend – among other things – on the volatility of the fuel and its composition.

The ability of diesel fuel to self-ignite is expressed in the cetane number. The higher the cetane number the more easily spontaneous combustion will take place. The optimum cetane number is regarded as being 45 to 55.

If the engine receives a supply of fuel with too low a cetane number, a situation arises in which, of the total amount of diesel fuel injected into the cylinder during the power stroke, there is already a large portion present when the first droplets begin to self-ignite. Once combustion has started in this way the rest of the fuel will instantaneously ignite and the pressure inside the cylinder will rise too fast and too far.

The result is a 'knock' (diesel knock) similar to the 'pinking' of a petrol engine, and characterised by a metallic banging noise. The tendency to knock also depends on the operating temperature of the diesel engine. In a cold engine, the fuel will find it harder to ignite and the engine starts to rattle.

Another important quality demanded of diesel fuel is low viscosity, or in other words a high degree of liquidity. The 'thinner' the fuel, the smaller the droplets will be after injection, and small droplets burn better because there is enough oxygen around them for complete combustion.

Diesel fuel must be free from impurities. The fuel pump and injectors are precision items of equipment and are susceptible to damage from even the tiniest particle of dirt, which is why the fuel system includes a fine filter which has to be replaced at regular intervals.

Fuels and the environment

The combustion of fuel in the engine produces various types of gas which are passed into the air through the exhaust system.

Under ideal circumstances the combustion gases will contain no harmful substances. During the actual combustion process, hydrocarbons (CH compounds) together with oxygen (O) from the outisde air are converted into water vapour (H_2O) and carbon dioxide (CO_2), both quite harmless substances. Water vapour and carbon dioxide are also given off by people, animals and plants and are also naturally present in the atmosphere in large quantities. The fact that exhaust gases do contain harmful substances is usually the result of incomplete combustion.

Because the mixture supplied to the cylinders is sometimes too 'rich', i.e. too many hydrocarbons for too little carbon dioxide, the fuel burns only partially, and so uncombusted and even toxic hydrocarbons reach the air. Carbon monoxide also is produced: this is a toxic gas.

Combustion also produces nitrogen oxides (NO_x) which can be harmful under certain circumstances.

The amount of harmful substances that is produced depends to a great extent on the conditions under which the engine has to work. In a cold start for example, when the engine is deliberately supplied with a rich mixture, the percentage of carbon monoxide and uncombusted hydrocarbons in the exhaust gases is significantly greater than when the engine has warmed up.

On average, the amount of harmful substances which the engine produces is quite small, all according to the type of fuel the engine uses. The table opposite shows how much uncombusted hydrocarbons (CH), carbon monoxide (CO) and nitrogen oxides (NO_x) is produced by a petrol engine, a diesel and an LPG engine in a specific rest.

The figures serve to convey an idea of the environmental acceptability (or otherwise) of the various engines; in actual practice, the figures may often be different.

We have already stated that petrol contains lead compounds to give it a sufficiently high knock resistance. A part of this lead escapes into the atmosphere with the exhaust gases. Another part reaches the engine oil or is deposited in the exhaust system.

In general it can be said that lead compounds are harmful to health, and for this reason a maximum limit was recently imposed for the lead content of petrol – 0.4 grams per litre. Indications point to a further reduction of this limit in the future.

In the United States, the amount of carbon monoxide and hydrocarbons in the exhaust gases is restricted by the fitting of catalytic 'afterburners' which can maintain their effectiveness over a long period only if the car is run on lead-free petrol.

Typical Relative Values for Exhaust Emission in the EEC Test★			
Fuel	CO gram	CH gram	NO_x gram
Petrol	160	20	6
Diesel	8	2	4
LPG	12	11	6

★ The EEC Test is a standardised test that simulates driving conditions in heavy city traffic.

The average speed is 11.6 mph, maximum speed 30 mph. The test lasts 195 seconds and the test vehicle covers a distance of 0.62 mile (approx. 1100 yards). During the test, the exhaust gases are collected and analysed.

The total values for CO, CH and NO_x shown above are for the test carried out four times consecutively. Thus the total EEC Test comes to 4×195 seconds ($=13$ minutes).

The graph shows how average driving in urban traffic is simulated during the EEC Test.

The test begins with 10 seconds of engine idling (speed $=0$) followed by 18 seconds of travel: the car is accelerated in first gear up to 9 mph. This speed is held for 8 seconds, the car is then braked to a standstill and the engine idles for 21 seconds. After this, the car is accelerated through gears 1 and 2 to 20 mph at which the speed is maintained for 25 seconds, then the car is braked, and so on to the end of the test.

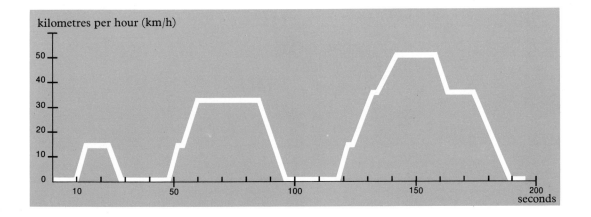

89

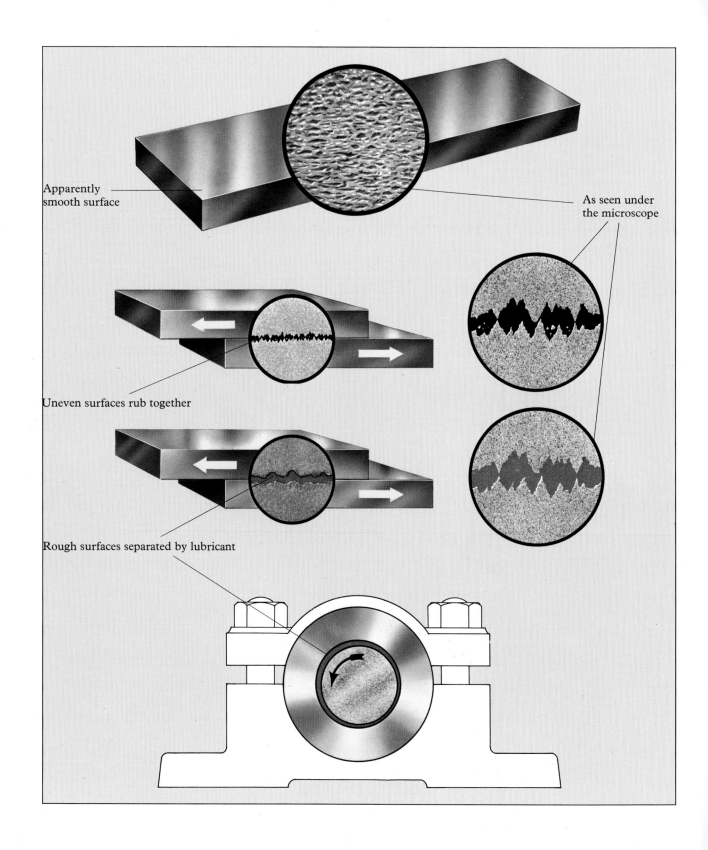

Apparently
smooth surface

As seen under
the microscope

Uneven surfaces rub together

Rough surfaces separated by lubricant

Lubrication

Good lubrication can mean the difference between life or death for an engine. If the engine is wrongly or inadequately lubricated, much damage can be caused; and without lubrication the engine will 'seize' in a matter of seconds.

The importance of lubricants becomes clear if we look at a piece of metal under a microscope. The surface may appear smooth to the naked eye but is, in actual fact, highly uneven. When two such surfaces rub together – like the piston rings that glide up and down the cylinder walls – the irregularities in the metal surfaces set up a resistance.

Called friction, this resistance can have disastrous consequences. First of all, energy is needed to overcome it, and this energy is converted into heat. Friction can cause extremely high temperatures which eventually will 'weld' together the irregularities of two parts moving in contact. The sheer speed of the motion tears off the irregularities, making the surfaces even rougher.

Another consequence of friction is wear. The irregularities rub against each other, the projecting points are broken off and the tiny metal particles act like abrasive sandpaper.

Friction and wear can both be alleviated by separating the surfaces with a lubricant – oil, for example. Oil forms a thin film that keeps the hard surfaces apart from each other so that they 'float' over the oil.

Apart from actually lubricating, oil fulfils three more important tasks.

Some engine parts get hot, not only by friction, but also by the heat that is given off during combustion. Pistons are a good example of such parts, and their heat has to be dissipated otherwise the metal would expand and the piston would stick fast in the cylinder. So the lubricating oil also serves to cool these hot parts.

Next, oil is used to seal, especially the space between the pistons and the cylinder walls to prevent combustion gases from getting through to the crankcase. Lastly, oil is used to trap impurities and combustion residue caused during the burning of the mixture in the cylinder.

Apart from the actual engine, a car has a number of other components which have to be lubricated: the gearbox, the differential, the wheel bearings, steering system etc.

Parts in which gear wheels are used are mostly lubricated with oil. Most of the other parts requiring lubrication have tended in recent years to be fitted with self-lubricating bearings which require no maintenance throughout the vehicle's life.

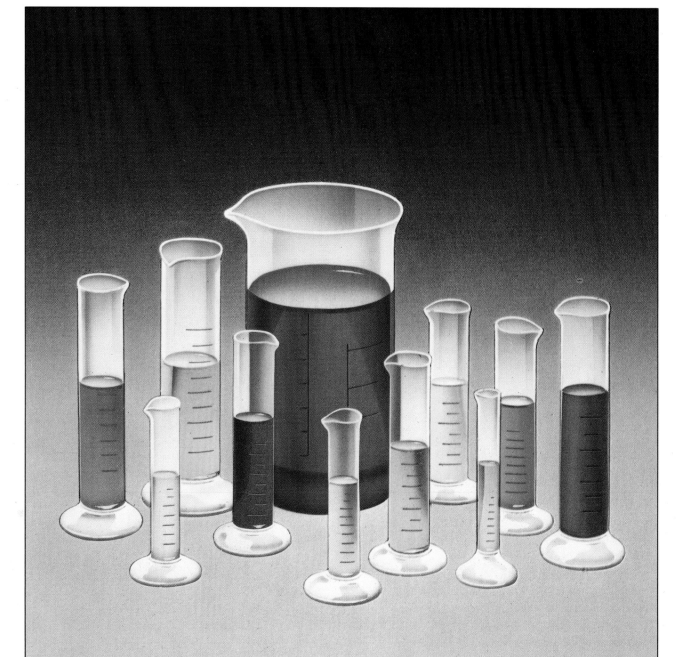

A good engine oil is a blend of oil and various additives that ensure that the engine's condition is maintained for as long as possible

Engine oil

Practically all car engines are lubricated by the so-called 'force feed' system. The oil in the sump is sucked by a pump which forces it along oilways leading to the crankshaft bearings, the bearings of the camshaft and the valve mechanism.

The oil that is forced to the crankshaft bearings splashes past, forming an oil mist which lubricates the cylinder walls and other parts, including the pistons, which are thereby cooled. Then the oil falls back into the sump and commences the process again, after passing through an oil filter that traps dirt and other impurities.

An engine oil has a lot to live up to. It must work in widely varying temperatures; it is polluted by the gases given off during combustion, and it is diluted by fuel which is not fully burnt after a cold start, i.e. before the engine reaches working temperature.

The properties of an engine oil can be classified in two systems:

1. The API (American Petroleum Institute) classification. This classification states the application for which an engine oil is suitable.
2. The SAE (Society of Automotive Engineers) classification. This classification indicates the viscosity of an oil.

Let us have a closer look at both these systems.

Quality (API classification)

The quality of an engine oil is expressed by the API classification which consists of two series, the S series for oils for petrol engines; and the C series, for diesel oils. These series are in turn subdivided into a number of categories: five for the S and four for the C series at the present time.

The categories are identified by letters of the alphabet, each of which indicates a different quality. The S series has SA, SB, SC, SD and SE, while the C series contains CA, CB, CC and CD. Most of the oils for petrol engines in cars currently on the market fall in the SE category. It is expected that there will soon be oils that can be allocated to a higher category, SF.

The quality of the oil is determined by a number of factors, one of which is the oxidation stability, i.e. the extent to which the oil resists ageing.

With the high temperatures prevailing in a car engine, the oil is able to combine chemically with the oxygen present in the air (oxidation). The resulting oxidation products cause the oil to thicken and deposit on certain engine components. So oxidation stability determines how long the oil's given viscosity is maintained.

Engine oil also has to have a detergent and a dispersant action, by which we mean that the oil must prevent the formation of sludge in the sump which otherwise would settle in the crankcase and other parts of the engine. (Sludge is formed when soot and water produced by combustion emulsify with the oil.)

A good engine oil will contain a number of additives intended to combat other undesirable phenomena. Anti-foam additives prevent foam from forming in the sump, while anti-wear additives reduce wear and tear on cams and camshaft. Anti-rust additives stop metal surfaces corroding; and finally there are alkaline compounds to neutralise acids in the oil that are caused by combustion.

SAE classification of motor oils

Engine lubricants are classified in viscosity classes according to their 'liquidity'. There are two main groups, namely the thin, easy-flowing oils (low viscosity) and the thick, 'syrupy' oils (high viscosity).

Each group is in turn broken down into classes which are indicated by a number. The higher the number, the thicker the oil.

For the group of thinner oils, the viscosity limits are set at a temperature of minus 18°C. This group of very 'liquid' oils is also identified by the letter W behind the number, which stands for 'winter operation'. Oils in this group are SAE 4W, 10W, 15W and 20W.

For the group of highly viscous oils, the viscosity limits are determined at 100°C. It includes SAE 20, 30, 40 and 50 oils.

The SAE classification was first introduced in 1911, and it made it possible for the motor manufacturer to give precise directions as to which lubricant was best suited to his product, and under which circumstances. Subsequent developments in lubricant technology have facilitated the production of oils which satisfy the requirements of both categories, i.e. at both low and high temperatures. These are oils, in other words, which cover several SAE classes, and are thus called multigrade oils. Some examples of these multigrade oils include SAE 10W/30, 10W/40, 15W/50, 20W/40 and 20W/50.

The SAE group uses a simple number or numbers to state the viscosity range of an oil. It does not say anything about the other characteristics of the oil, e.g. its adhesive properties to metals, its chemical or thermal stability, its degree of corrosion protection, detergency and so forth.

The API classification tells us more about these qualities. The benefits of a multigrade engine oil are not hard to grasp. Its liquidity ensures a rapid start and immediate lubrication, thus minimising wear after starting from cold. Fuel consumption is also favourably influenced because the engine feels less resistance from the cold oil. Since the oil retains thickness as the temperature rises, there is optimum lubrication under high engine loads and at high temperatures.

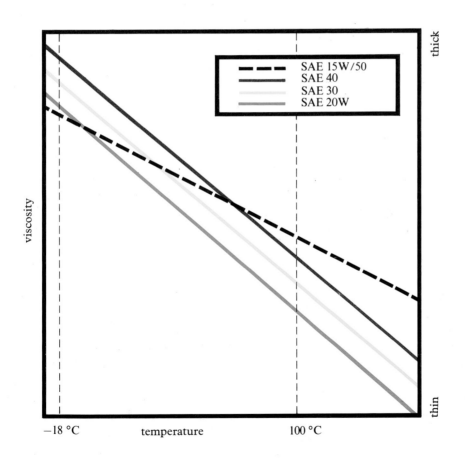

Viscosity-temperature response of engine oils with different SAE ratings

Fault-finding

A car is a complex piece of machinery, so the risk of a breakdown is always present. But it is not always easy for the not-so-technically-minded motorist to trace the cause of a failure. Just as in a detective novel, it is a matter of trial and error, of thinking logically where the problem might be located and then ruling out the least likely possibilities.

This chapter is limited to minor engine faults: starting difficulties, trouble on the road and so on. Bigger problems and defects with items like the brakes, steering and transmission are best left to the experts since the average motorist may be unable to remedy the situation properly. Our hints are also based on the most common type of car, i.e. no diesel engines or petrol engines with fuel injection, electronic ignition etc.

The engine fails to start

The biggest and at the same time most frequent problem – the engine that makes you wait – can be solved only by tackling the situation in systematic fashion. We have therefore presented our hints in the form of 'programmed instructions'. You begin with Check 1 and continue until you have traced the trouble.

1. Is the engine turning?

Many people fail to distinguish between 'not starting' and 'not turning'. If you try to start and the starter motor does not even rotate the engine then there is clearly something wrong with the battery or starter motor circuit. However, if the starter motor turns normally but the engine fails to fire, then the problem is elsewhere.

Yes – proceed to 2
No – start at 1a

1a. Switch on the headlights and try again
You should enlist the aid of another person to see what happens to the headlights while you turn the ignition key. Four things can happen:

I. There is a 'clicking' sound from under the bonnet and the lights go out
In this case it is very likely that one of the battery terminal connections is defective. Remove the battery cables and clean the terminals throughly. Then replace the cables and tighten them firmly. Also check the earth connection – this is usually the cable that runs from the minus battery terminal to the car body or chassis.

II. The headlights dim to half their usual brightness

This means that there is too little current being supplied by the battery and it has to be recharged or replaced. You can do the recharging process yourself if you possess a battery charger; otherwise (or if you do not have the time) you will have to ask someone else to give you a tow or a 'jump' start. If you can get a tow or a push, release the clutch smartly with second or third gear engaged. Don't forget first to turn on the ignition, and be careful that once the engine starts it does not run you forward into the towing vehicle. To charge the battery fully once the car is going takes a drive of at least half an hour if your car has an alternator. With the older kind of direct current dynamo it can take two or three hours of driving. The alternative technique of starting a car with a flat battery is to use suitable heavy duty leads with large clips (called 'jump leads', and available from car accessory shops). Connect your car's battery to that in a friend's car. Connect positive to positive, negative to negative, and use your starter in the ordinary way, while the engine of the other car is running.

III. The headlamps burn normally

There is probably a loose connection somewhere. Fig. 1 shows which connections you should check. If you still cannot trace the fault it is likely that the ignition switch or the starter relay is defective.

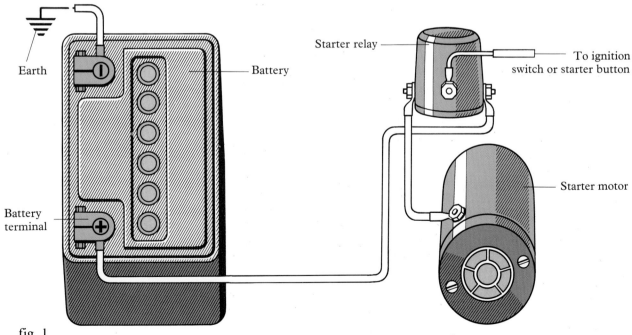

Earth

Battery

Starter relay

To ignition switch or starter button

Starter motor

Battery terminal

fig. 1

IV. The headlamps do not burn at all (not even if you do not turn the ignition key to the starter position)

In this case, the battery is completely 'flat', probably because a part of the car's electrical equipment has been 'left on', e.g. the lights. As in II, the battery has to be recharged. A tow start or a 'jump' may succeed, but for a tow or push start it will be necessary for the speed to be sufficient to bring the alternator into operation (at least 20 mph), sustained for several seconds, since the battery cannot even provide enough current for the ignition coil.

Note that tow starts are not usually possible for cars equipped with automatic transmission, because unless the engine is running there is no drive to the hydraulic pump which energises the transmission system. A 'jump' start from a serviceable battery will be necessary, as explained earlier.

2. Is the ignition system damp?

This often seems to be the cause of the problem of failure to start, especially in cold and wet weather. Have a look under the bonnet and check whether any parts of the ignition system appear damp. Sometimes the whole under-bonnet area may be running with condensation. We assume that the engine is not 'flooded'. This misleading term is applied to an engine in which unvaporised petrol has condensed on the sparking plug electrodes, preventing any spark from occurring. To 'clear' a flooded engine, press the accelerator pedal slowly right down to the floor and keep it there, check that the choke control is pushed right in, and give a good long run on the starter. A 'flooded' engine should then start.

Yes – start at 2a
No – proceed to 3

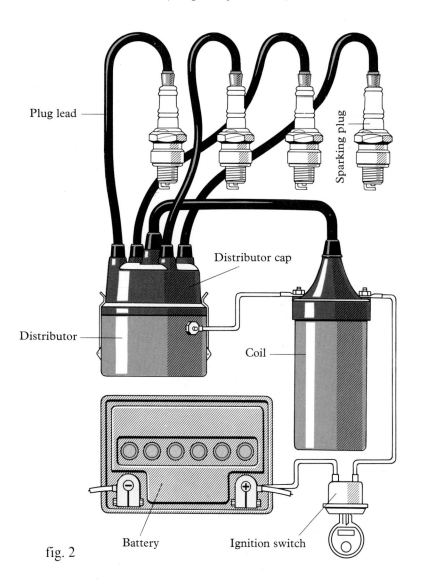

Plug lead

Sparking plug

Distributor cap

Distributor

Coil

Battery

Ignition switch

fig. 2

2a. Dry out the ignition system

In the first chapter of this book we saw that the ignition coil creates a current of approx. 15 000 volts. This current must make a spark jump the gap between the electrodes – a distance of around 0.7 mm – under a gas pressure that is about 10 times greater than atmospheric pressure. It is logical for the electric current to follow the line of least resistance. Normally the high tension parts of the ignition system are very well insulated, but dampness can affect the insulation and then current may leak from the plugs to earth. This problem can be overcome by drying out the system with a dry cloth or absorbent tissues. Alternatively, spray with an anti-damp product that can be bought in an aerosol can. Fig. 2 shows which wires and connections should be dried in this way.

3. Is there a spark at the plugs?

Detach a plug lead from the plug and insert a screwdriver with an insulated handle into the cap at the end of the lead. Hold the metal shank of the screwdriver about a quarter of an inch from a convenient earthed point, e.g. the engine block. Ask someone to turn the ignition key to the starter position and see whether a spark jumps the quarter-inch gap (fig. 3). (Make sure your hand is away from the metal part of the screwdriver, otherwise you will receive a sharp but harmless shock. Also watch out for the rotating fan.)

Yes – start at 3a
No – proceed to 4

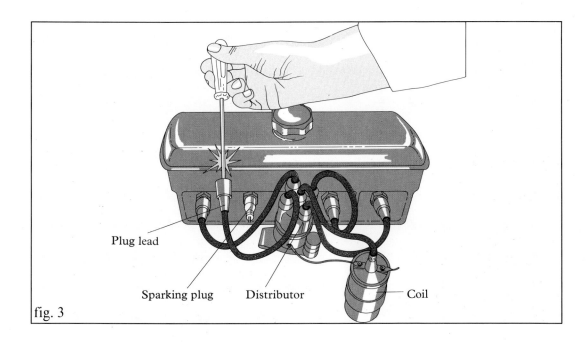

Plug lead

Sparking plug   Distributor   Coil

fig. 3

fig. 4

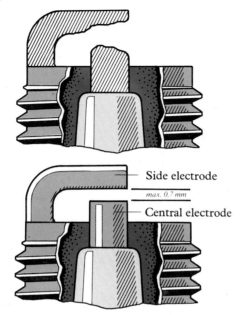

Side electrode

max. 0.7 mm

Central electrode

3a. Repair or replace the sparking plugs

It may be that the plug electrodes are burnt, in which case the gap between them will be too wide for the spark to jump it (fig. 4). This can be remedied by removing all plugs and tapping the side electrode in towards the central electrode. The gap should not exceed 0.7 mm (0.027 in). If you do not possess a 'feeler gauge', tap the side electrode in until you can just fit your thumbnail between the electrodes. The nail is of course thinner than 0.7 mm, but that does not matter. To prevent connecting up the plug leads to the wrong plugs, it is wise to deal with each plug in turn, re-connecting its lead after replacement. Take care that dirt cannot get into the cylinders through the plug holes. If you are unable to repair the plugs in this way, they will have to be replaced by new ones, preferably all at the same time. If you do this yourself

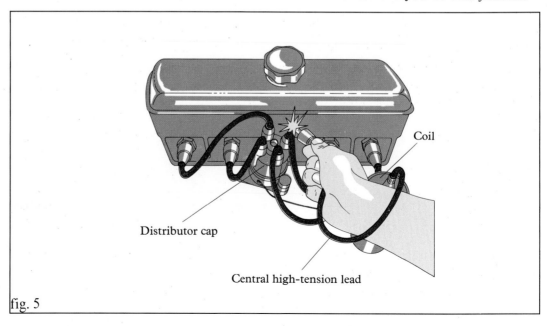

Coil

Distributor cap

Central high-tension lead

fig. 5

make sure you buy the right plugs for your type of car. To prevent damage to the screw thread by 'cross-threading' it is wise to screw the plugs in as far as possible by hand before tightening with a suitable tool. Do not over-tighten.

If the engine still fails to start, proceed to 7.

4. Is there current at the high tension cable?

Reconnect the sparking plug leads and pull the central high tension lead from the coil out of the distributor head (fig. 5). Hold the end of this cable a quarter of an inch from the engine block and see if there is a spark when the ignition switch is operated.

Yes – start at 4a
No – proceed to 5

4a. Check distributor head and rotor

If there is current at the high tension cable but none at the plugs, it is likely that the fault lies in the distributor. Remove the distributor head by releasing the clips or screws that hold it to the distributor body (fig. 6), and examine the inside of the head for cracks which can trap moisture or carbon deposits, across which the current can 'leak'. A fractured distributor head will have to be replaced at the first opportunity. It can sometimes help to seal the crack with nail varnish to enable you to reach home or a garage. The rotor may also be cracked and must be replaced, but this rarely happens.

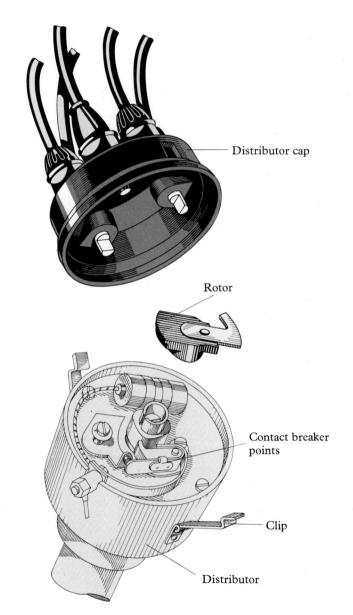

Distributor cap

Rotor

Contact breaker points

Clip

Distributor

fig. 6

101

5. Check the primary circuit

By 'primary circuit' we mean the coil, the contact breaker and the cables between them. This is best done with the aid of a test lamp that can be purchased cheaply in any car accessory shop. The lamp is mounted inside the handle of a probe resembling a screwdriver, which is also fitted with a length of wire and a spring clip which can be clipped to the earth. When the point of the probe is brought into contact with a point supplied with current from the battery, the lamp lights up. To check the primary circuit, the earth clip must be clipped to the earth and the tip of the probe brought into contact with either end of the thin wire which runs from the side of the distributor to the coil (fig. 7).

(Check first that the lamp is in fact working, by testing where you are sure there is current, e.g. across the terminals of the battery.)

If the engine is now turned, one of three things will happen:

Lamp goes on and off – start at 5a
Lamp does not go on – proceed to 5b
Lamp stays on – proceed to 6

5a. Coil defective

If the lamp goes on and off the contact breaker is working properly. If the car still does not start and you have carried out all the previous checks correctly, the only possibile ignition failure left is a faulty coil or condenser which will have to be replaced. However, failure of either of these is rare. Double-check for other causes of trouble first.

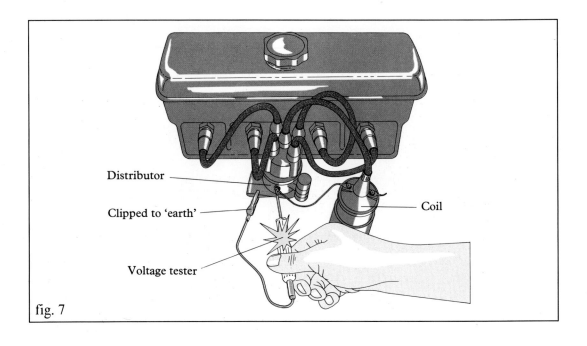

Distributor

Clipped to 'earth'

Voltage tester

Coil

fig. 7

5b. Check the current supply to the primary circuit

The question now is whether the fault is in the contact breaker or in the circuit supply. To check this, the thin wire between coil and distributor has to be disconnected at one end, preferably at the distributor end, although this is not always possible (fig. 8). Connect the spring clip of the lamp tester to the terminal from which you have just disconnected the wire. When the point of the tester is brought into contact with the loose end of the wire the lamp should burn continuously when contact is made.

Lamp fails to light – start at 5c
Lamp lights up   – proceed to 6

5c. Refit the loose wire

It is now clear that there is something wrong with the current supply in the primary circuit of the ignition system. There is probably a loose connection somewhere, perhaps at the ignition switch. If you are unable to find the loose connection there is an easy provisional remedy. Simply fit a wire from the battery terminal which is *not* connected to earth to the coil terminal i.e., the one which is *not* connected to the distributor (fig. 9).

This will by-pass the loose connection and the engine will start.
Note : Leave the ignition key in the switch (in its normal driving position) for as long as the engine is running, otherwise the steering lock will operate.

Once you have arrived home, you will have to disconnect the provisional wire in order to stop the engine.

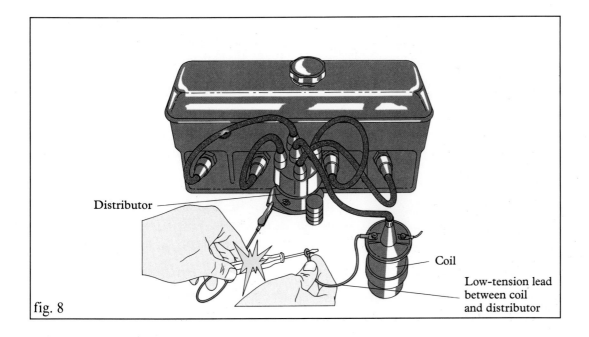

Distributor

Coil

Low-tension lead between coil and distributor

fig. 8

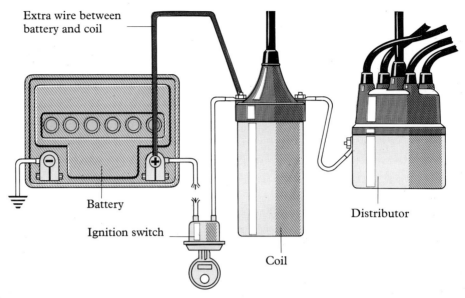

Extra wire between
battery and coil

Battery

Ignition switch

Coil

Distributor

fig. 9

Contact breaker screw

Condenser

Fibre block

Spring

Contact
breaker points

Distributor

Low-tension terminal

fig. 10

6. Check the contact breaker points

If the fault lies in the contact breaker points, one of three things may be wrong:

a. they do not open
b. they do not close
c. they short-circuit

To get at the points, you have to remove the distributor cap by loosening its clips or screws, as described above. Lift up the cap and move it to one side (it should not be necessary to disconnect the plug leads). Now remove the rotor, which is a push fit on the distributor shaft, simply by pulling upward. When re-fitting, remember to locate the tongue on the rotor into the slot at the top of the distributor shaft.

Once the rotor has been removed, we can – with most, but not all, distributors – look down on the contact breaker points (fig. 10). When the engine is turned over, the points should be seen to open and close quite distinctly.

6a. Points do not open
If the points do not open, the fibre block which passes over the cams on the distributor shaft is worn down. Fortunately, the remedy is fairly simple:

1. Engage top gear.
2. Push the car backwards or forwards until the fibre block is opposite one of the highest points of the distributor cam.
3. Take a screwdriver and slacken off the screw which holds the fixed contact point to the circular plate in the distributor.
4. Push the fixed contact point over the plate so that the points are opened and set the gap to approx. 0.5 mm (0.015 in, or about the thickness of a postcard).
5. Now tighten the screw firmly, ensuring that the contact point gap stays the same.
6. Re-fit the rotor and the distributor head and the engine should now start.

It is advisable to have the contact breaker gap and the 'timing' of the ignition checked by a garage, after this has been done.

6b. Points do not shut
If you can see that the points never touch each other, i.e. do not make contact, then the little spring which closes them is defective. In this case, the contact breaker points have to be replaced, and this is better done by a garage.

In most cases however, the points will appear to close but still fail to make contact. This means that they are dirty or burnt, in which case the simple remedy is to purchase a contact point file in any car accessory shop, insert the file between the points and file them flat. Re-fit rotor and distributor head, and the problem is solved.

6c. Points short-circuit
Since the fixed contact point is connected to earth, it is obvious that the moving point is completely insulated in the distributor. If this insulation is now damaged in one way or another, the points will short-circuit and will fail to do their job, because there will be no current supply to interrupt.

The insulation can be damaged at the following places:

1. The nut which connects the wire from the coil to the distributor is attached with the aid of fibre washers. These washers may be damaged.
2. The spring which connects the nut referred to above with the moving contact point in the distributor may be damaged and touching earth.
3. The little wire connecting the condenser with the same nut may be shorting to earth, due to defective insulation.
4. The condenser may itself be defective, but this is rare.
5. The fibre bush which insulated the moving contact point from its pivot

pin may be damaged, but this too is a rare occurrence.

Once you have located the short-circuit and made the necessary repairs/replacements, re-fit rotor and distributor head, and the engine should start.

7. Is there petrol at the carburettor?

Most starting problems are due to ignition faults; but if the ignition system is found to be working properly and the engine still does not start, there may well be a problem with the fuel supply, e.g. an empty petrol tank, a blocked hole in the petrol cap, a blocked fuel line or filters or even a defective fuel pump. A mechanical fault is also theoretically possible, but this may make itself known by some unusual noise, for example if the camshaft drive is defective, but this is extremely unlikely.

To check the supply of petrol it is best to disconnect the pipe which runs from the petrol pump to the carburettor. When the engine is turned, spurts of petrol should come from the carburettor end of the pipe, showing that the fuel supply to the carburettor is in order.
Note: Watch out for any risk of fire during these checks.

Yes – proceed to 8
No – start at 7a

7a. Check the petrol pump
If no petrol comes from the pipe, then the petrol pump is presumably defective. To be absolutely certain it is just as well to check that the pipe itself is not blocked. This is unlikely however, since a particle of dirt is not able to block the pipe completely.

The petrol pump is either mechanical or electric. Mechanical pumps are driven by the engine and so, of course, work only when the engine is turning. An electric pump used to supply fuel when the ignition was switched on, but on some cars they now operate only when the engine is actually turning, thereby reducing the risk of fire in event of an accident. There are three things that can be checked on a mechanical pump:

a. a loose cover nut which allows air to get into the pump. Tighten the bolt firmly but not to the extent that pump cover and gasket are deformed;
b. the gasket under the cover may be damaged, also allowing air into the pump (replace gasket);
c. the fuel filter may be completely blocked and will have to be cleaned out.

If there is still no supply of fuel after these three points have been properly checked, then the pump diaphragm, diaphragm spring or valve springs may be defective. All these components are supplied as a complete set and will have to be replaced.

8. Check the carburettor

If the pump is indeed supplying fuel, it may be that the needle valve in the carburettor is sticking, with the result that petrol cannot get into the float chamber. This problem can usually be overcome by giving the float chamber a sharp tap with the handle of a screwdriver. If this does not help, the cover screws will have to be removed in order to reveal the needle valve. In this instance you can forget the notorious 'blocked jet' since nearly every carburettor has more than one jet. For example, if the main jet is blocked then the engine will still idle. If the idle jet is blocked, however, the engine will run well when the accelerator pedal is depressed but will stall when the pedal is released.

Trouble on the road

The most common mishap which can occur once the car is running is that the engine suddenly cuts out, in which case the same procedure applies as for an engine that will not start in the first place. Look in particular for wires adrift, which could account for sudden failure. When going over the ignition system, give the contact breaker points an extra thorough check.

It often happens that the fibre block on the contact breaker arm is worn down with the result that the points do not 'break', a problem that is quickly solved by adjusting the points as described above.

The engine overheats

One problem that can happen after a long period of 'crawling' in urban traffic queues, a steep climb on a mountain road or with a low coolant level is that the engine overheats, and this can be seen from the water temperature gauge, a warning lamp or from escaping steam.

The remedy will much depend on the type of car that you have. If your car has a sealed cooling system there is no general rule that can be applied, and you will have to refer to the owner's manual. However, if the radiator has a cap which can be removed by hand you have an open cooling system, in which case proceed as follows. Pull off the road, stop the engine and let it cool down for fifteen minutes or so. Then place a double-folded cloth over the radiator cap and slacken it off a little to let the steam escape – but be ready to jump clear.

Once all the steam has escaped, remove the cap completely and wait for any boiling water to run off before topping up the radiator with fresh water. Take care! A stream of cold water into an engine that has been severely overheated can do irreparable damage. Add the water gradually, at intervals. Be ready for it to heat rapidly to boiling, and come gushing back out. If you think that the over-heating was severe, wait at least an hour until the engine has had a chance to cool down properly. Signs of such severe over-heating are smoking, paint burning on exposed engine parts, and ominous clicking noises.

Once the radiator has been topped up, it is wise to trace the cause of the overheating to prevent a recurrence. In most cases, the cause will be leakage or possibly a radiator cap that is defective or which does not close the radiator off correctly. The cap is so made that the cooling system is always under a certain pressure, which raises the boiling point of the water (from 100°C to, for instance, 110°C).

During a long, hard climb the temperature of the coolant may well rise above 100°, but nothing will happen so long as the radiator cap is in order. If it is defective, then the coolant's boiling point will be 100° with the result that the water will boil and turn to steam.

There may be other reasons why the engine is overheating, such as a slack fan-belt, dirt in the radiator or water jackets, partial blockage of water hoses or a defective water pump. Even if no spare fan-belt is available, a makeshift one can be made out of a nylon stocking tied firmly round the fan-belt pulley and the pulley which drives it. This provisional belt need not be tied around the dynamo as well, since the battery is able to supply current for a short period of time without being charged.

A water hose may split on the road. If the split is small, then the leak can be temporarily stopped with insulating tape. A large split is more difficult to cope with, and it may help to wind material such as an inner tube or plastic around the hose and make it fast at either end with wire.

Remember that if you have topped up a leaky radiator with water you should add anti-freeze as soon as possible after repair, to prevent corrosion and freezing.

Vapour lock

This is a phenomenon that rarely occurs these days but is not totally ruled out. It happens at very high ambient temperatures when the air beneath the bonnet is 'suffocating'. What happens is that somewhere in the fuel pipe the petrol is vaporised at a 'hot spot' exposed to high heat radiation from the engine, and this pocket of vapour stops the smooth flow of fuel. The remedy is simple: just make the petrol pump thoroughly wet, which will cool the fuel vapour and turn it back to the liquid state. If the trouble recurs you can tie a sponge around the fuel pump and keep it wet.

Index